47   ट)

I HAVE
FIVE DAUGHTERS

A Morning-Room Comedy
in Three Acts made from
Jane Austen's novel
PRIDE AND PREJUDICE

by

MARGARET MACNAMARA

SECOND EDITION
(Revised)

SAMUEL   FRENCH

LONDON
NEW YORK SYDNEY TORONTO HOLLYWOOD

MADE AND PRINTED IN GREAT BRITAIN BY
BUTLER & TANNER LTD, FROME AND LONDON

NOTES FOR THE PRODUCER

PERIOD

Pride and Prejudice was written in 1797, when Jane Austen was twenty-two years old ; it was revised and published in 1813. There is nothing in the novel to fix the date of its happenings more nearly than that. Mr. Bennet refers to his " powdering gown," but the name is sure to have been used for years after the use of powder in hair-dressing had died out.

ETIQUETTE

For the bows and curtsies of the period, reference may be made to *Manners and Movements*, by Isabel Chisman and E. Raven-Hart, published by H. F. W. Deane & Son. People rarely shook hands. Slight bows and curtsies sufficed for ordinary greetings of welcome and farewell.

Mr. Collins habitually bows—more deeply than the occasion requires. Mrs. Bennet curtsies deeply to Lady Catherine. Between Charlotte and the Bennet girls, the curtsies are hardly more than bobs, though less jerky.

Girls rose from their seats on the entry of their elders (fathers included) and remained standing till the elders were seated, unless told to sit.

When paying a call, a gentleman brought hat, stick and gloves into the morning-room in his left hand, and held on to them unless he was invited to put them down ; then he laid them on the floor beside his chair ; never on a chair or table. During a first call, which lasted about ten minutes, he would not expect to be relieved of them.

SETTING AND FURNITURE

The demands of the text upon the setting are as simple as they probably would have been had Jane Austen herself dramatized her novel. Essentials are as follows :

1. Two tall sash-windows with six panes in each frame.
2. A panelled door up stage on the actors' left.
3. Double half-glazed doors into a conservatory on the actors' right.

The walls may be completely papered, or panelled and painted, with wallpaper filling the centre of the panels. Among possible types of wallpaper that known as " flock," which originated as an imitation of brocade, is the easiest to represent.

If the stage manager cannot possibly visit a museum or a mansion where Georgian rooms and furniture may be studied at first hand, he should seek illustrated books in the local Free Library. Good ones to ask for are : *The Encyclopædia Britannica, Old English Furniture for the Small Collector* by Blake and Revers-Hopkins, published by Batsford ; *Collecting Antiques* by Felix Gade, published by T. Werner Laurie ; *Historic Wallpaper* by N. V. McClelland.

COSTUME

Many excellent books on costume have been published in recent years. The essentials are given in a nutshell in coloured drawings, by Iris Brooke, in *English Costume in the Eighteenth Century*. Patterns may be found in *Dress Design* by Talbot, published by Pitman, and *A History of Costume* by Koehler and Sichart, published by Harrap. The designer should remember that Miss Bingley is the only fashionable lady in the play and that English country gentry have never sacrificed comfort and common

3

sense to the demands of the dictators of Paris fashions. Illustrators of Jane Austen's novels are inclined to favour the styles in vogue when her later works were written, but she must have imagined the characters in *Pride and Prejudice* in late eighteenth-century dress—1796–7.

ACKNOWLEDGMENTS

My thanks are due to Messrs. Joseph Williams for kind permission to use one line from my one-act comedy, *Elizabeth Refuses*, drawn from the same novel and published in 1926.

For closely detailed criticism and a number of ingenious suggestions, I am indebted to my sister, Helena Norris Mack, M.A. (Oxon).

The second edition owes much to purposeful watching of Miss Caryl Jenner's direction of the rehearsals of Miss Sally Latimer's Amersham Players.

M. M.

CHARACTERS

*Jane Austen does not seem to have been precise in her own mind as to the ages of Mr. and Mrs. Bennet. They have been married long enough to have a daughter of twenty-two ; it is highly improbable that Mrs. Bennet was more than twenty on her wedding day. There is no evidence of any marked difference between their ages.

SYNOPSIS OF SCENES

ACT I
The morning-room at Longbourn. A morning in February.

ACT II
SCENE 1.—The same. A morning in early March. Eleven days later
SCENE 2.—The same. A morning in late March. Three weeks later.

ACT III
The same. A morning in late July. Four months later.

I HAVE FIVE DAUGHTERS

ACT I

The morning-room at Longbourn in Hertfordshire, the residence of MR. BENNET, *whose income is about £2,000 a year. The aspect of the room is "full west," with two tall sash windows, commanding a view over a small, private park. On either side of the windows the wall turns, to face north-west and south-west and accommodate two doors ; that on the north-west leads into the passage, that on the south-west into the conservatory. Since the play is "naturalistic" the fireplace has to be shown, but the source of the glow from the fire should be masked from the audience by a low, standing fire-screen.*

The furniture should be Chippendale or Hepplewhite rather than Sheraton. Essential pieces of furniture are : a settee, placed R., *below the conservatory door and above the fireplace, which is well down stage ; a small circular table, placed* L. ; *a writing-table, against the left wall ; several chairs ; one or two stools ; one or two small, firm cushions.*

A sunny morning in February. The five MISSES BENNET *are present.*

JANE *is beautiful and of a singular sweetness of character. To "great strength of feeling" she unites "composure of temper and a uniform cheerfulness of manner." A detractor criticized her for smiling too much.*

ELIZABETH *has "fine dark eyes" and "a lively, playful disposition," which "delights in anything ridiculous." She is her father's favourite.*

MARY, *"the only plain member of the family," is near-sighted, round-shouldered and lumbering in gait ; her complexion is dull, her hair thin and straight. Recognizing that her exterior gives her no chance of competition with her sisters in looks, she concentrates on earning a reputation for accomplishments, "deep reflection" and impeccable rectitude. Disdained by both her parents, she is the odd man out among the sisters.*

KITTY, *"slight and delicate," readily becomes fretful ; she is under the domination of her younger sister.*

LYDIA, *her mother's favourite, is a sturdy, "well-grown girl of fifteen, with a fair complexion and good-humoured countenance." She has high animal spirits and abundance of self-assurance.*

JANE *is at work on a large canvas, stretched on a frame.* ELIZABETH *is hemming a lawn handkerchief.* MARY, *armed with notepaper and pencil, is studying an enormous calf-bound book.* KITTY *and* LYDIA *are whispering and giggling together on the settee, without pretence of employment.*

MARY. Elizabeth! Would you recommend this passage for my album of "Elegant Extracts"? "Notwithstanding the almost universal prevalence of a contrary opinion, it is——"

ELIZABETH. One moment, Mary. Has anybody seen my scissors? Jane, have you?

JANE. No. These are my own.

ELIZABETH. Kitty! Have you borrowed my embroidery scissors—and without leave?

KITTY. No.

ELIZABETH. Have you, Lydia?

LYDIA (*nonchalantly*). Oh, I believe I did. I'd forgotten. You might help look, Kitty.

(*The two start a perfunctory search.*)

JANE. Sit nearer me, Lizzy, and share my scissors till yours turn up.

(ELIZABETH *moves her chair.* KITTY'S *search takes her to the mantelpiece,* LYDIA'S *to the window near the conservatory. By standing with her back to the south, and peering out of the window in a north-westerly direction,* LYDIA *can see a wide sweep of the drive.*)

LYDIA. Oh, I do wish I could see two or three officers strolling up the drive to pay a call!

KITTY. Oh, so do I! There's nothing in the world so bright as a red coat and gold epaulettes shining in the sun!

ELIZABETH. And nothing so dull as the conversation of most of your dandies in the militia. What do you say, Jane?

JANE. I find them very good-humoured, Elizabeth.

ELIZABETH. Of course you do! Your willingness to like everybody you meet naturally puts them in a good humour!

LYDIA. Oh, oh, what do I see? A red-coat! A red-coat!

KITTY (*dashing to her side*). An officer coming to call! . . . Where? Where? I can't see him!

LYDIA. He ran up the oak-tree!

KITTY. A squirrel?

LYDIA. Squirrels have red coats, don't they?

KITTY (*slapping her lightly*). You are silly, Lyddie!

(MRS. BENNET *comes in, sending her voice before her. She is a bouncing, vigorous woman in the early forties, who has retained more of her early beauty than is usual among her contemporaries. "A woman of mean understanding, little information and uncertain temper . . . when she is discontented she fancies herself nervous. . . . The business of her life is to get her daughters married; its solace visiting and news.*")

MRS. BENNET. Girls! Girls! What are you all about? Lyddie and Kitty, didn't the dancing-master urge you to practise the deep curtsy? Come away from the window!

LYDIA. I'm hunting for Elizabeth's scissors. (*As if trying to recollect.*) I was cutting a piece of rather thick string—oh, I remember now!—the stupid things broke—snapped across one of the blades!

ELIZABETH. Lydia! You are aggravating!

MRS. BENNET. Stop quarrelling, Lizzy! I cannot stand your noise! You should put your things where no one can find them if you're so mean you can't lend 'em to anybody! Mary, you'd better join in the dancing practice. Get to your places, the three of you! And don't open your mouths! This incessant chatter would wear out the patience of a saint! Mary! How many thousand times am I to tell you?—put your shoulders back and your head up and your chin in! The more I plague myself to teach you to be graceful, the more awkward you grow! Now then—ready! One, two, bend lower—lower—down—down——"

(LYDIA *grabs* KITTY *and thrusts her against* MARY. *The three sprawl on the floor.*)

LYDIA (*as she falls*). Don't, Kitty, don't!

KITTY. I didn't! It was you pulled me!

MARY. I'm not to blame!

MRS. BENNET. You naughty children! Have done with this romping! Cease giggling, will you? Get up off the floor!

KITTY (*still on the floor, weakly giggling*). Aow—a stitch in my side!

MRS. BENNET. Get up off the floor! Upon my word! Me with my nerves in such a state I'm not fit to be out of my bed and you encouraging Lyddie to tumble about and laugh!

JANE (*signing to* KITTY *not to defend herself*). Might I superintend the curtsy practice, ma'am—while you rest?

MRS. BENNET. Rest—rest—how can I rest with my head in such a whirl?

JANE. Would a little turn in the garden refresh you?

MRS. BENNET. Be quiet, Jane! This continual worrying at me upsets me more than anything!

(LYDIA *is still on the floor.* MARY *and* KITTY *have scrambled up and moved out of her reach.*)

LYDIA. Aow! A stitch in both my sides!

MRS. BENNET. Lyddie, I've had enough of this! I've a good mind to send you to your room for the rest of the day! And no dinner but dry bread!

LYDIA (*as she rises, sulkily*). You can't send me to my room, ma'am! Now that I've " come out," I'm not to be treated as if I was a child!

Mrs. Bennet. Haven't I declared all along you were too young to come out ?

Elizabeth (*with an air of innocence*). Surely it was Jane and I who said that, ma'am ?

Mrs. Bennet. Oh, of course, Jane and you had to be selfish ! Just when the militia was suddenly quartered near by, for the first time in twenty years, you and Jane were all for denying my poor Lyddie the least share in the fun !

Lydia. Officers are *such* fun, aren't they, ma'am ? Always ready to flirt.

Mrs. Bennet. There was a time—when first I came out—I'd hardly look at a civilian !

Lydia. I'd sooner flirt with one officer than twenty civilians !

Mrs. Bennet. Like me when I was your age ! Who knows what might have happened if your granny hadn't warned me again and again that officers in the militia are notorious for having to live on their pay. Men of means are only to be found in the regular army.

Lydia. Oh, when I fall in love—properly in love—not flirting, he'll come into a large fortune !

Mrs. Bennet (*genuinely touched by a sentimental memory*). That's how it was with your papa.

Elizabeth. He was an only son, we have to remember.

Kitty (*beginning on a rather timid note*). Ah, but when a true lover isn't an only son—old uncles and people make wills and hide them in queer places where they get found.

Elizabeth. Ah, yes, for that belief there are numerous authorities in the circulating library.

Mrs. Bennet. Don't nag, Lizzy !

Mary. I have read somewhere that facts are often stranger than fiction. Are they not, mamma ?

Mrs. Bennet. An excellent proverb !—We're wasting time ! Back to your places, you three, and begin !

(*The* Servant *announces* Miss Lucas. Charlotte *is a " sensible, intelligent young woman of about twenty-seven. . . . Elizabeth's intimate friend." She is no beauty, but* Mrs. Bennet *exaggerates in pronouncing her " very plain."*)

Ah, Charlotte, my dear ! How is Lady Lucas ? I thought you were to be busy all morning with the orange marmalade !

Charlotte. Good morning, ma'am ! Good morning, all ! Mamma has spared me for a few minutes to take the air.

Mrs. Bennet. You have news, I do believe !—Sit down, I beg !—Is it about this young Mr. Bingley who has just taken Netherfield Park ?

Charlotte. Has Mr. Bennet not yet called upon him ?

Mrs. Bennet. No ! And vows he never will ! A single young gentleman with three or four thousand a year ! The first moment I heard of it—" What a fine thing for our girls ! " I said. And straight away Mr. Bennet began refusing to call on him.

CHARLOTTE. This morning Mr. Bingley has returned papa's call.

MRS. BENNET. Oh, of course Sir William Lucas was to the fore, though he has but the two daughters !

JANE. Is Mr. Bingley a pleasant person ?

ELIZABETH. Is he amusing ?

LYDIA. Is he likely to join the army ?

KITTY. Is he fond of dancing ?

MARY. Is he well-informed ?

CHARLOTTE. Listen, please—the exciting thing is that he turns out to be the very young man Jane and I thought he might be.

MRS. BENNET. What young man did you think he might be ?

CHARLOTTE. And his manners are every bit as amiable as we agreed he looked.

MRS. BENNET. Oh, what is this mystery ?

CHARLOTTE. Didn't Jane tell you ?

JANE. There was nothing to tell.

MRS. BENNET. Then why keep it secret ?

CHARLOTTE. Have I your permission, Jane ?

JANE. Of course.

CHARLOTTE. Last Saturday Jane and I were passing the tobacconist's in the market-place at Meryton when a flock of sheep obliged us to take refuge in the doorway. A moment later a very gentlemanly young stranger stepped out of the shop.

LYDIA. Bingley, was it ?

MRS. BENNET. Ah !

CHARLOTTE. He, too, waited for the sheep to pass and glanced at Jane. And though he was not so ill-bred as to stare, he stole another glance—and yet another.

MRS. BENNET. Did he speak ?

CHARLOTTE.⎫
JANE.   ⎬ Oh no !

MRS. BENNET. So this Mr. Bingley has already begun—there's a fact for you, my dear Jane. " Stranger than fiction."

ELIZABETH. Is it strange that a young man should find Jane better worth looking at than a passing sheep ?

MRS. BENNET. Don't be vulgar, Lizzy—I'm surprised you should fancy it witty to compare your sister to a farm animal. When the whole neighbourhood acknowledges that if Jane were not so over-modest and fastidious she'd have been married long before she reached twenty-one.

ELIZABETH. Twenty-*two* is her age, ma'am.

MRS. BENNET. Hold your tongue, Lizzy. You delight in provoking me. My nerves—— !

LYDIA. Oh, go on, Charlotte. How old is he ?

CHARLOTTE. Twenty-three, I gathered. But I'm not at the end of my story.

(*Interest is renewed with* " Oh ! " *and* " Ah " !)

When Papa introduced him to me this morning I couldn't resist saying, " We have met already——" and I described the occasion. Very gallantly he declared he remembered me. And most ungallantly he added, " You had a younger lady with you."

(ELIZABETH *joins her in light laughter.*)

MRS. BENNET. Jane, of course. (*To* JANE.) There now, my dear ! Did he ask her name and all about her ?

CHARLOTTE. Unfortunately my father addressed him on some other topic, and he lost the chance.

MRS. BENNET. What a terrible pity ! But is he handsome ?

CHARLOTTE. Very good-looking, wouldn't you say, Jane ?

JANE. No one could deny it.

LYDIA. I spy a wedding in the family—*at last* !

KITTY. May I be bridesmaid, Jane ?

JANE. Mamma, please check Kitty and Lydia.

MRS. BENNET (*petulantly*). Good gracious, whatever for ? But you three younger ones had better go out for a walk while the sun is high.

MARY. I shall wander in the park, and ruminate on what I have read.

LYDIA. We'll go into Meryton, Kitty—and stand in the doorway of the tobacconist's, like Jane ! An officer may come out !

(LYDIA *and* KITTY *giggle themselves off into the hall.*)

MRS. BENNET. Listen to me, Jane. Next time you meet Mr. Bingley, think what you are about or you may live to be sorry, for nothing will come of it.

ELIZABETH. How can anything " come of it," ma'am ? Papa refuses to call on Mr. Bingley, to make his acquaintance.

MRS. BENNET. I shall never stop teasing him till he does.

CHARLOTTE. Mr. Bingley is to be at the next Assembly Ball. Mamma will introduce him to you.

MRS. BENNET. I don't believe she will. She has her own daughters to get off.

CHARLOTTE. Mamma has no hopes on our account, I assure you. Neither have I.

MRS. BENNET. Anyhow, an introduction at a public ball gets us nowhere. He dances with Jane once, or at most twice, and there it ends. (*Very grudgingly.*) He'll dance with you, no doubt.

CHARLOTTE. It would have been almost rude if he hadn't given me to understand he meant to ask me for the first dance.

MRS. BENNET. The first dance at a public ball is the most marked attention a young gentleman can offer.

CHARLOTTE (*laughing and with complete sincerity*). It will soon be forgotten on both sides !

ELIZABETH. Charlotte, I have a favour to ask ! A pot of Lady Lucas's marmalade to use as a bribe. Papa is for ever grumbling at our housekeeper's orange marmalade——

(MR. BENNET *has come in and heard the last sentence. " An odd mixture of quick parts, sarcastic humour, reserve and caprice," he long ago decided that he could endure the folly of his wife only by making her the butt of his wit. She is quite incapable of understanding most of his remarks.*)

MR. BENNET. The statement is false, Lizzy. I deny that I am " for ever " grumbling at anything.

(*He bows to* CHARLOTTE *and she curtsies.*)

MRS. BENNET. Lizzy is provoking me to death, Mr. Bennet.

MR. BENNET. I should consider it my duty to grumble for some hours, my dear, if her wit had such a melancholy consequence.

ELIZABETH (*as winningly as she is able*). We were discussing, sir, whether I could bribe you with a pot of Lady Lucas's orange marmalade to call on the new tenant at Netherfield Park.

MR. BENNET. Not with all the pots in Lady Lucas's storeroom ! Not by any bribe on earth can I be induced to call upon Mr. Bingley.

MRS. BENNET. Oh, it's too bad ! No consideration for my poor nerves !

MR. BENNET. I am come from my library, Mrs. Bennet, to convey to you the purport of this letter which I received a few days ago.—Don't hurry away, Miss Lucas.

CHARLOTTE. I fear I must. . . . I was on the point of going. . . . I will take the short cut.

(ELIZABETH *opens the conservatory door for her. She is soon gone, but probably overhears the first sentence of the next speech.*)

MRS. BENNET. It's a very disagreeable habit, Mr. Bennet, to praise up other people's orange marmalade—and only done to vex me. (*As soon as the door is shut.*) That spiteful Charlotte called here on purpose to boast she's to be Mr. Bingley's partner for the first dance at the Assembly Ball. Mr. Bennet, how much longer are you going on refusing to call on the most promising young man within reach of us ?

MR. BENNET. For as long as you continue to plague me, my dear.

MRS. BENNET. If I stop plaguing you, will you ?

MR. BENNET Listen to me, please. (*Flourishing a letter.*)

A month ago I received a request from a young clergyman to pay us a visit. A fortnight ago I replied. He will arrive to-day, Monday—within the next half-hour—and stay until Saturday week.

MRS. BENNET (*sulkily*). A young clergyman ?

JANE. Who can he be ?

ELIZABETH. How well do you know him, papa ?

MR. BENNET. I have never seen him in my life.

MRS. BENNET. A total stranger—a man you know nothing about ? And you've invited him to stay for a fortnight !

MR. BENNET. He invited himself. His stay is to be for twelve days. His letter contains a considerable amount of information. (*He uses the letter merely to refresh a good memory.*) He is the incumbent of a valuable parish—no, " a valuable rectory "—the parish carries little weight—a valuable *rectory* in the gift of one Lady Catherine de Bourgh, whose " bounty and benevolence " he hopes to reward by " demeaning " himself ever " with grateful respect."

ELIZABETH. Had you ever heard of him before ?

MR. BENNET. I had. Within a few hours of his birth, I learnt of the happy event and knew him to be the heir to a considerable property.

MRS. BENNET. Young, did you say ?

MR. BENNET. Twenty-five.

MRS. BENNET. Married, I suppose ?

MR. BENNET. Single, I infer.

MRS. BENNET. Ho ! (*Sparkling.*) A bachelor with a handsome stipend—and heir to—is he likely to inherit his property within a few years ?

MR. BENNET. I sincerely hope not !

ELIZABETH. Oh, why grudge a young clergyman his inheritance, papa ?

MR. BENNET. Because he will step into it over my grave.

MRS. BENNET (*with a shriek*). What ?

JANE. Oh, papa !

MR. BENNET. This Mr. Collins stands next in the entail. When I die he can turn you all out of the house as soon as he pleases.

MRS. BENNET. Oh, your odious cousin Collins, is it ? I do think it's the hardest thing your estate should be entailed away from your own children. If I had been you, Mr. Bennet, I should have tried long ago to do something or other about it.

JANE. Nothing can be done, ma'am.

MRS. BENNET. I've been told that a thousand times !

ELIZABETH. Females don't count as descendants.

MRS. BENNET. Be quiet, both of you ! What could be more cruel than to settle an estate away from a family of five daughters to a man nobody cares anything about ?

Mr. Bennet. If you listen to Mr. Collins' letter you may be a little softened towards him.

Mrs. Bennet. I am sure I shall not. I think it was very impertinent of him to write to you at all. And very hypocritical. Why couldn't he keep on quarrelling with you as his father did before him ?

Mr. Bennet. Why, indeed, he did " fear it might seem dis-respectful to his father's memory to be on good terms with one with whom it had pleased him to be at variance." But, " having become a clergyman," he flatters himself that his " overtures of goodwill are highly commendable." He begs leave to apologize for being " the means of injuring " my " amiable daughters " and assures me of his readiness to make them " every possible amends."

Mrs. Bennet. There is some sense in that.

Jane. What amends could he make ?

Mr. Bennet. If he married my widow——

Mrs. Bennet. For shame, Mr. Bennet.

Elizabeth. Can he be a sensible man, sir ?

Mr. Bennet. No, my dear, I think not. I have great hopes of finding him quite the reverse. There is a mixture of servility and self-importance in his letter that promises well. I am impatient to see him.

Mrs. Bennet. I must speak to the housekeeper about pre-paring a bedroom.

Mr. Bennet (*near the window*, R.). First I must claim your attention for another matter.

Mrs. Bennet. Oh, what is it now ?

Mr. Bennet. I have just observed from the window that Mr. Bingley is approaching by the footpath.

Mrs. Bennet. Mr. Bingley ? Incredible !

Mr. Bennet. Why so ? I find no great difficulty in believing that he is about to return my call.

Mrs. Bennet. What ? You *have* called ?

Jane.
Elizabeth. } Oh, sir !

Mrs. Bennet. In spite of declaring you wouldn't !

Mr. Bennet. Pardon me, I did not explicitly declare I would not until after I had.

Mrs. Bennet. Oh ! Oh ! Such a good joke to play upon us ! I knew you loved your girls too well to neglect such an acquaintance. How pleased I am !

Mr. Bennet. I observed another young gentleman with Mr. Bingley. You must try to find out, Mrs. Bennet, whether he, too, is unmarried and what he is worth.

Mrs. Bennet. I will indeed ! What an excellent father you have, girls ! Two young gentlemen ! Three, if that odious Mr. Collins turns out to be not so odious after all. Jane, how beautiful you look! Lizzy, you are almost as pretty as Jane!

(*Instinct, rather than reason, prompts these compliments, and instinctively the two girls play up. The* SERVANT *announces* MR. BINGLEY *and* MR. DARCY. BINGLEY *is " good-looking, with easy, unaffected manners." His ductility of temper endears him to* DARCY, *who is correspondingly dominating. With a " fine, tall person, handsome features and noble mien,"* DARCY *cannot but be admired ; but as he is " haughty, reserved and fastidious, his manners are continually giving offence."*

It should be noted that the etiquette of the country house permits the resumption of needlework within a few minutes of a visitor's arrival.)

MR. BENNET. Delighted to welcome you, Mr. Bingley. Allow me to present you to my wife——

MRS. BENNET. Charmed, sir—my eldest daughter—my daughter Elizabeth——

(*Bows and curtsies are accompanied by very cordial smiles.*)

BINGLEY. Allow me to present my friend, Mr. Fitzwilliam Darcy, of Pemberley House in Derbyshire.

MR. BENNET. I am honoured, sir!

MRS. BENNET. Any friend of yours, Mr. Bingley——

(DARCY'S *bows are so haughty that to welcome him warmly is impossible.*)

MR. BENNET. Be seated, gentlemen!

MRS. BENNET. Oh, Mr. Bingley, Miss Lucas has been telling us how she met you in the midst of a flock of sheep, and how gallantly you behaved!

BINGLEY. I should have rejoiced, madam, had there been any occasion for gallantry. . . . If I am not mistaken, Miss Bennet was with Miss Lucas at the time!

MRS. BENNET. Was she indeed ? You never mentioned a word of it, Jane!

JANE. No, ma'am! . . . How, Mr. Bingley, do you think you will like this neighbourhood ?

BINGLEY (*eyeing her*). Beyond expression!

MRS. BENNET. Netherfield Park is one of the most admired residences within half a day's drive of London town. But if it were a palace, I'd pity any young gentleman with only a house-keeper to look after his comfort.

BINGLEY. This very afternoon the control will be taken over by my sister. She is several years older than I, and thoroughly experienced in directing housekeepers.

MRS. BENNET. I shall be prodigious pleased to call on Miss Bingley!

BINGLEY. How kind you are ! I am enchanted by the civility I receive on all sides ! Sir William Lucas has been most obliging !

MRS. BENNET. Oh, a Sir William Lucas is bound to be obliging, seeing he owes his knighthood to the luck of being mayor of our little town at the time of a royal visit ! His daughters are very good sort of girls, I assure you. It's a pity they're no beauties. Not that I think Charlotte so very plain, but then she is our particular friend.

BINGLEY. She seems a very pleasant young woman.

MRS. BENNET. Oh, dear, yes, but you must own she is very plain ! . . . Have you a long tenancy of Netherfield Park, Mr. Bingley ?

BINGLEY. A year.

DARCY. Some months of the year, Bingley, you intend to spend in London. Do not forget that for part of the Season I shall be occupying my house in Mayfair, and I have your promise to be my guest.

BINGLEY. I shall look forward with eagerness to fulfilling the promise. You, Miss Bennet, expect to be in town for the Season ?

JANE. Oh, no ! Now and then we do stay with an uncle and aunt, but they live in Gracechurch Street. (*Pronounced* " Gracious Street.")

BINGLEY. Is that far from Mayfair ?—I'm from the north, and a stranger to London.

DARCY. Gracechurch Street is in the City.

MR. BENNET. My wife's brother lives over his shop.

BINGLEY. Oh ?—ah ! (*Plunging with a deprecatory glance at* DARCY.) So did my father until he had made his money. I've told you before, Darcy, how when I was still in petticoats I couldn't be cured of climbing over the packing-cases, and got properly——

ELIZABETH. Spanked.

BINGLEY. Properly spanked, as you say.

MRS. BENNET. Lizzy, I'm surprised at you ! It's very inelegant to make your father laugh like that before company.

ELIZABETH. Forgive me, ma'am ! Mr. Bingley hesitated for a politer word. In the absence of ladies the reminiscence ends with a spanking.

MRS. BENNET. Hush ! I wish to be heard ! Talking of a Season in town, I believe, Mr. Bennet, it would be the very thing for my poor nerves.

MR. BENNET. I foresaw that was the topic on which you wish to be heard, Mrs. Bennet.

MRS. BENNET (*viciously*). All you care about is to order a parcel of books from Booksellers' Row. And if they are brown and ragged with dust, so much the better——

BINGLEY. Reading is your hobby, sir ? Darcy's collection of

books at Pemberley House is one of the finest in Derbyshire. He'd sooner spend a wet morning with a book in his library than a fine morning with a gun on his moors.

MRS. BENNET (*to* DARCY).   Then I hope, sir, that *Mrs.* Darcy is fonder of books than I am.

BINGLEY (*as* DARCY *merely stares*).   Mr. Darcy is a bachelor, madam.

MRS. BENNET.   My second daughter is the one who is allowed in her father's library, Mr. Darcy.   (DARCY *bows slightly*.)   You mustn't judge from her nonsensical chatter, for she often reads a book.

ELIZABETH.   Nearly always a novel.

MRS. BENNET.   Whatever it be, you know you can talk very clever about books, even cleverer than Jane.

MR. BENNET.   Not in a manner to give pleasure to a student, my dear.

ELIZABETH.   Mr. Darcy doesn't reckon novels to be books— do you, Mr. Darcy ?

DARCY.   Novels, I admit, seldom cause me to waste my time on them.

MRS. BENNET.   Then my third daughter, Mary, must be mentioned.   Mary is like you for despising novels.   She'll sit all day with her nose in the dreariest volumes you ever saw in your life !

(*A gush of giggles from the passage is followed by the headlong ingress of* KITTY, *propelled by* LYDIA.)

KITTY.   Oh, Lyddie, don't !

MRS. BENNET.   For shame, Kitty !   That's not the deportment you've learned from your dancing-master ! . . . My youngest and next-to-youngest—Mr. Bingley—Mr. Darcy— Lydia—Kitty !

BINGLEY.   How happy you must be to have four daughters, Mrs. Bennet !

MRS. BENNET.   Five, sir—just now I mentioned Mary.

BINGLEY.   Ah, yes, yes !

MR. BENNET.   Stop giggling, Lydia ! . . . Occasionally, Mr. Bingley, I forget that I have five daughters.   My wife is never out in her reckoning.

MRS. BENNET.   La, Mr. Bennet, you're poking fun !

(LYDIA, *still childish enough to be embarrassed by strangers, and always in some awe of her father, has sought refuge on the settee beside her mother.   Determined to capture attention, she bursts into loud, hurried description of her latest experience.*)

LYDIA.   Ma'am !   We met Colonel Forster and his girl-bride, and the Colonel mocked at us for walking into Meryton when all our special dandies chance to be on duty !

KITTY. So we turned back, but——

LYDIA. But first I made the Colonel give me the name of that handsome new officer Elizabeth saw yesterday getting off the coach !

MRS. BENNET. What's this ? Elizabeth, you never told me of a handsome new officer getting off the coach !—Well, Lyddie, what is his name ?

LYDIA. Wickham.

KITTY. And he comes from a place called Pemberley in Derbyshire.

MRS. BENNET. Goodness gracious !—Pemberley in Derbyshire ?—where you come from, Mr. Darcy ! So you know this Mr. Wickham, and can tell us all about him !

DARCY. Pardon me, I do not know Mr. Wickham.

BINGLEY. Surely you know everyone at Pemberley.

DARCY. I have dropped this particular acquaintance.

MRS. BENNET. La, now !

LYDIA. What a shame ! Whyever ?

MRS. BENNET. We must have an explanation ?

DARCY. It is quite unnecessary to explain.

LYDIA. Oh, but we shall tease you till you do !

JANE (admonishingly). Lyddie, dear !

ELIZABETH. Isn't it a little unfair, Mr. Darcy, to announce that you have dropped a man's acquaintance, and refuse to give your reason ?

DARCY. In my view it is generous to the person in question.

BINGLEY. You may rely upon it, Miss Elizabeth, Darcy would never drop a Pemberley man without very good cause.

MR. BENNET. Perhaps you, Mr. Bingley, have some notion what the cause may be ?

BINGLEY. None whatever ! But I can vouch for the right judgment of my friend.

MR. BENNET. Humph ! As a rule in this locality any new-comer to the regiment is welcomed with open arms. Would Mr. Darcy deprive Mr. Wickham of the privilege of mingling in Meryton society ?

DARCY. Certainly not, sir. My responsibilities do not extend beyond my own county. A year ago I washed my hands of the fellow. For me he no longer exists !

LYDIA. Heavens, how horrid for poor Mr. Wickham !—And there's Elizabeth quite put out—she's wild to dance with him !

ELIZABETH. Nonsense, Lydia !—Absurd !

LYDIA. I heard you tell Jane—you didn't know I was by !

ELIZABETH. Never in my life have I said I was wild to dance with anybody !

LYDIA. Your exact words were, " He's the handsomest man I ever saw ! " You said it twice !

ELIZABETH. Well ?

JANE. That's entirely different!

LYDIA. And instead of scrambling off the top of the coach (like all the officers *I've* ever watched), " he vaulted down and bounced on his toes so neatly he must be a fine dancer! " So there! That's what Lizzy told Jane!

MR. BENNET. Upon my word, Elizabeth, I shall begin to think you as silly as Lydia and Kitty.

ELIZABETH. It was all nothing, sir!

MRS. BENNET. La, Mr. Bennet, you can't expect girls to have the sense of their mother! . . . Mr. Bingley, have you heard what's afoot in Meryton the day after to-morrow ?—a ball in the Assembly Rooms!

BINGLEY. Sir William Lucas informed me. I hope to take my sister and, of course, Mr. Darcy. You will be there, I trust ?

MRS. BENNET. No question!

LYDIA. *We* shall be there! Every one of us!

MRS. BENNET. Though it's not for *my* pleasure or comfort, I assure you! Late hours and noise and confusion and the military band pounding away—how I face the fatigue I never know, but I'm the last person to consider myself when young people are full of their own happiness.

BINGLEY (*sympathetically if perfunctorily*). Ah, h'm!—Miss Bennet, for the first dance, unluckily—that is, for the first dance I am engaged to Miss Lucas. For the second, may I venture to hope I may have the honour of your hand ?

JANE. I shall be pleased, sir ?

LYDIA. I and Kitty are all booked up to the officers! I'm sorry now I didn't reserve one on the chance, because of Wickham.

BINGLEY. Darcy, *you* are a fine dancer—much better than I. You'll seize this opportunity to insure against being left out in the cold ?

DARCY. " The cold " has no terrors for me, I thank you! I detest dancing unless I am very well acquainted with my partner.

BINGLEY. Then the only lady who will suit you for a partner at this ball is my sister ? (DARCY *does not reply*.) You don't intend to idle about whenever she is dancing with someone else ?

DARCY. To " idle about " with my own thoughts is infinitely preferable to the falsity of sustaining a flow of trivial conversation with a stranger.

BINGLEY. You amaze me, Darcy! How can a man with your strength of character let himself be so easily overcome by shyness ?

DARCY. Shyness ?

ELIZABETH. Why not ? 'Tis a weakness permitted to students. Novelists write of " a shy student " as they do of " a spoilt boy."

MR. BENNET. Or " a pert girl," eh, Elizabeth ?

ELIZABETH. No, sir, " an innocent girl."

DARCY. I lay no claim to the title of "student," madam. But I refuse to admit that a gentleman makes himself ridiculous by cultivating a taste for serious reading and purposeful conversation.

BINGLEY. You are serious and purposeful about so many things ! . . . Mr. Darcy came into his inheritance at the age of fifteen, and has toiled ever since at fulfilling the duties of a large landowner. The prosperity of the farmers, the relief of the poor, the schooling of the children, the punishment of the immoral women and the poachers ! Not content with merely being a magistrate he frequently consults some weighty volume on the law. You ladies will hardly credit the trouble I had to persuade him to let Pemberley take care of itself for a couple of weeks while he became my guest in Hertfordshire.

DARCY. Since feudal times a certain tradition of care for the estate and its people has been followed at Pemberley.

LYDIA. Mr. Bingley !—when are you going to give us a ball at Netherfield Park ?

BINGLEY. I haven't yet thought about giving a ball.

LYDIA. Can't you think about it now without delay ?

BINGLEY. To-morrow I will—as soon as my sister arrives. I must consult her.

LYDIA. Please let it be one day next week !

KITTY. Oh, do !

MRS. BENNET. For a small private dance there is no occasion for more than a few days' notice.

LYDIA. There, sir ! You *will* make it one day next week—— Promise !

KITTY. Please, please !

MR. BENNET. Enough ! You two are as forward as you are foolish ! Be off for your walk, and don't dare to plague Mr. Bingley again !

BINGLEY. Oh, sir, I beg you——

MRS. BENNET. The poor girls meant no harm.

(*Already* KITTY *and* LYDIA *have reached the door, which their father holds open for them.* KITTY *is a little tearful ; even* LYDIA *is crestfallen. As the door into the hall is shut upon them, the double doors of the conservatory are opened and* MARY *stumbles in.*)

Ah, here is Mary ! The one I spoke of as so devoted to dull reading—Mr. Darcy ! Mr. Bingley !

MR. BENNET. You could have guessed for yourselves that Mary is the accomplished member of the family.

(MARY, *missing her father's malevolent intention, smirks and curtsies.*)

MRS. BENNET. Step forward, my dear Mary.

Mr. Bennet. You are in the nick of time, child, to join Kitty and Lydia in their walk.

Mary. I have just come in, sir.

Mr. Bennet. Catch them up and check their silly behaviour if you can.

Mary. Nobody can, not even Elizabeth.

Mr. Bennet. Try.

(Mary *goes out into the hall and he shuts the door on her.*)

Mrs. Bennet. Mr. Bennet, what has Mary done to provoke you ? I cannot understand your ways.

Jane. May I venture the suggestion, sir, that the gentlemen might like to be shown your library ?

Mr. Bennett. My books are not worth inspection by the owner of one of the finest libraries in Derbyshire.

Darcy. Its assembly has been the work of generations of my ancestors. But I am a very inexperienced collector. I shall be grateful, sir, for the privilege of viewing your treasures.

Mr. Bennet (*melting towards a fellow book-lover—for him a rara avis*). One or two oddments on my shelves I do prize rather highly.

Darcy (*sincerely eager*). May I see them ?

Mr. Bennet. Come with me, sir.

Darcy. Come, Bingley.

Bingley. I'm a complete ignoramus, you know. (*He is looking at* Jane, *but her eyes are bent on her embroidery.*) But I shall be glad to learn.

Mrs. Bennet. You girls are going too !

Jane.
Elizabeth. }No !
Mr. Bennet.

(*After bowing to the ladies, who remain sitting and respond with bows, the two young men go out, followed by* Mr. Bennet.)

Mrs. Bennet. Oh, you two—you vex me beyond bearing with your stand-off airs ! I wear myself to a shadow on your behalf, and you sit there as prim as a pair of wax images !

Jane. Might I help you, mamma, by seeing about the bed-room for Mr. Collins ?

Mrs. Bennet. No, you might not ! I'm perfectly capable of remembering about the bedroom for Mr. Collins, and I don't want any interfering busybody giving orders to my housekeeper, 1 thank you !

(Jane *has opened the door for her ; she sails out.*)

Elizabeth. Oh, Jane !—How *can* mamma behave as she does ?

Jane. Her nerves do make her inclined to be irritable.

ELIZABETH. I don't mind her nerves ! It's her way of fishing for eligible young men with a great trawling net ! Mr. Darcy obviously saw what she was about.

JANE. Oh, I hope Mr. Bingley didn't ! Don't you think he's too modest ?

ELIZABETH. Of course I don't ! Neither do you !

JANE. We ought not to forget that with all five of us on her hands at once, mamma has cause to feel anxious.

ELIZABETH. The chief cause for anxiety is Lydia's disgraceful behaviour, which mamma encourages !

JANE. Lizzy, dear, I own I'm terribly ashamed of Lydia, but——

ELIZABETH. The whole visit was horrid ! Even papa was ungentlemanly—sneering at mamma, and holding Mary's plainness up to ridicule !

JANE. We ought not to be finding fault with our parents like this !

ELIZABETH. I am to blame, not you ! Indeed, you are the one and only member of the Bennet family who is invariably well-bred.

JANE. I'm longing to hear your opinion of our new neighbour and his friend.

ELIZABETH. Oh, Jane, what a man !

JANE. He is extremely agreeable.

ELIZABETH. I meant Mr. Darcy !

JANE. He certainly is—less pleasant.

ELIZABETH. Never in my life have I met anyone who so roused my antagonism at first sight.

JANE. My impression of Mr. Bingley is just the opposite.

ELIZABETH. " I detest dancing unless I am very well acquainted with my partner." That is, unless the lady belongs to the Pemberley circle of wealth and rank. He can't stoop to the common politeness of " trivial conversation " with an " outsider." Such pride is insufferable !

JANE. Mr. Bingley called it shyness.

ELIZABETH. Shyness is pride—his form of it anyhow !

JANE. From what Mr. Bingley said, Mr. Darcy was burdened with the ownership of Pemberley when he was very young, and accepted his duties most conscientiously. For some years, I suppose, he has been a magistrate and consulted volumes of the law.

ELIZABETH. And revelled in punishing the immoral women and the poachers. Long before he came of age, he started to domineer over everybody who was in his power. It's plain there is no one at Pemberley to laugh at him and tease him and stick pins into him as I should love to do. If I were his sister I'd " go for " the bully !

JANE Mr. Bingley's sister is several years older than he. I have a presentiment that I shall like her.

ELIZABETH. Conscientious Mr. Darcy may be in improving his estate and his people, but he is not above slandering poor Mr. Wickham behind his back.

JANE. That's quite unfair, Lizzy! We know nothing of the cause of the quarrel.

ELIZABETH. I'll vouch for it Mr. Darcy was in the wrong—and outrageously insolent.

JANE. Lizzy, you are letting prejudice run away with you. We really have nothing against him but that his manners are cold and haughty, and that he failed to ask you to dance when it seemed to us that he ought to.

ELIZABETH. The set of his mouth is against him. You cannot deny that the set of his mouth is very satirical. It provoked me into being impertinent. I had to say " spank " and hint that he was a spoilt boy, or I should have been afraid of him.—But he's not worth troubling about.—Did he behave so odiously because that is his nature, or because he disliked me ?

JANE. Lizzy dear, need you mind ? I never saw you so wrought up.

ELIZABETH. I don't mind ! I'm interested in studying an intricate character, that is all.

JANE. You have not said one single word about Mr. Bingley.

ELIZABETH. Mr. Bingley is very different.

JANE. He seems just what a young man ought to be ; sensible, good-humoured, lively. And with such happy manners ! So much ease with such perfect good breeding.

ELIZABETH. I agree. Your praise is fully deserved. I rather resent the fact that the much better man of the two is much the less handsome.

JANE. Is Mr. Bingley the less handsome ?

ELIZABETH. Did you not notice that he is ?

JANE. Perhaps. Anyhow, looks are unimportant. I liked immensely the way he spoke of his sister. One heard the affection in his voice, and a sweet deference.

ELIZABETH. Too sweet may be ! Certainly too sweet to Mr. Darcy ! Letting himself be led off to the library when he wanted to stay at your side !

JANE. I thought his going showed the most delicate tact. What struck me most about him was——

ELIZABETH (*in unintentional duet with the last sentence*). What struck me most about him was——

(*The confidences are cut short by the entrance of* MRS. BENNET, *who is pleasantly excited.*)

MRS. BENNET. Girls ! The chaise with Mr. Collins is just pulling up. After all, you may have been wise, Jane, in not going to the library. With your beauty you can afford to be a little reserved. But you must have a care ! I've known many an artful girl to over-reach herself. However, as the affair is shaping, I may safely congratulate you !

JANE. Mamma, dear——

ELIZABETH. You cannot congratulate me, I'm afraid.

MRS. BENNET. You lose nothing, my dear, by not suiting that Mr. Darcy's fancy.

ELIZABETH. I heartily agree with you, ma'am.

MRS. BENNET. So high and so conceited ! If he does ask you to dance with him in the end, I wouldn't if I were you.

ELIZABETH. I believe, ma'am, I may safely promise you *never* to dance with Mr. Darcy.

(MR. COLLINS *is announced by the* SERVANT. *He is " a tall, heavy-looking young man of five-and-twenty." Brought up by " an illiterate and miserly father who kept him in subjection," he " acquired a manner of great humility," now " a good deal counteracted by the self-conceit of a weak head, living in retirement, and the consequential feelings of early and unexpected prosperity." In a measure he caricatures* DARCY, *but whereas* DARCY *is arrogant and overbearing from the life-long habit of self-esteem,* COLLINS *is pompous and assertive from a secret doubt of his own real worth.* DARCY *owns no superiors ;* COLLINS *is abjectly obsequious to those who are above him in rank and wealth.*)

MRS. BENNET. Ah, Mr. Collins. *I* must welcome you at the outset, for Mr. Bennet is engaged in the library with a young gentleman of fortune who has just taken the largest house in the neighbourhood and is very amiable, and another even wealthier young gentleman, but we've no opinion of him.

COLLINS (*bowing repeatedly*). I must apologize, madam, for this intrusion.

MRS. BENNET. No, no. It's for Mr. Bennet *I* apologize.

COLLINS. My apologies are most sincere, believe me.

MRS. BENNET. My dear sir, it's for *you* to accept *my* apologies for the absence of your host.

COLLINS. Then I do, with alacrity, madam. . . . These are two of my fair cousins ?

MRS. BENNET. Jane, my eldest. Elizabeth, my second—Mr. Collins.

COLLINS (*bowing very low and more than twice*). Your servant, ladies—most happy.

MRS. BENNET. Be seated, Mr. Collins, I pray.

COLLINS. I will, most gratefully. (*He does.*)

JANE. Did you have a comfortable journey, sir ?

COLLINS. I am glad to assure you in the affirmative. In truth, I scarcely felt the jolting of the post-chaise, my mind was so fully occupied with the prospect of enjoying the society of my good cousin and his amiable wife and beautiful daughters.

MRS. BENNET. Had you heard of their beauty ?

COLLINS. I had. But it exceeds my expectations. No doubt before long these young ladies—and in due course the remaining three—will be well-disposed in marriage.

MRS. BENNET. I wish with all my heart it may prove so, for else they will be destitute enough. Things are settled so oddly.

COLLINS. You allude to the entail of this estate upon myself ?

MRS. BENNET. Ah, sir, I do indeed. Not that I mean to find fault with *you*, for such things I know are all chance in this world. There is no knowing how estates will go once they come to be entailed.

COLLINS. I am very sensible, madam, of the hardship to my fair cousins. And could say much on the subject but that I am cautious of appearing forward and precipitate. But I can assure *both* the young ladies that I come prepared to admire them.

MRS. BENNET. Ah !—Jane and Lizzy, Mr. Collins will excuse you—it is time you took the air in the park.

JANE. Yes, mamma.

MRS. BENNET. Drop your work and hasten out while the sun shines.

ELIZABETH. With pleasure, ma'am.

COLLINS (*rising and opening the door*). Perhaps my fair cousins would permit me to escort them.

MRS. BENNET. No, no, Mr. Collins, you are too gallant. You must rest from the fatigues of your journey. (*He is about to protest, but is checked by an emphatic stage-aside.*) I want a word with you.

(*He bows* JANE *and* ELIZABETH *out and returns.*)

COLLINS. I must apologize for not immediately comprehending the——

MRS. BENNET (*cutting him short*). You were saying you come prepared to admire my dear girls ?

COLLINS. In order that you may perfectly appreciate my motives in that respect, I must tell you that my patroness, Lady Catherine de Bourgh, to whose bounty and benevolence I owe the valuable rectory I have the honour to inhabit——

MRS. BENNET. Yes, yes——

COLLINS. Lady Catherine de Bourgh has advised me to marry.

MRS. BENNET. No advice could be better !

COLLINS. Twice has she condescended to give me her opinion on this subject—unasked too ! " Mr. Collins," said her lady-ship, " you must marry. A clergyman like you must marry ! "

MRS. BENNET. Any sensible woman would say the same.

COLLINS (*continuing conscientiously*). " Choose properly," said her ladyship. " Choose a gentlewoman for *my* sake, and for your *own* let her be an active useful sort of person, not brought up high but able to make a small income go a good way."

MRS. BENNET. H'm !

COLLINS. " Find such a woman as soon as you can, establish her in the Rectory and I will visit her ! "

MRS. BENNET. Very gratifying to be sure ! . . . And the " amends " you wrote of in your letter ?

COLLINS (*not to be diverted from his prepared speech*). Being as I am to inherit this estate on the death of your excellent husband —who, however, may live many years longer——

MRS. BENNET. Indeed I hope so !

COLLINS. I resolved to choose a wife from among his daughters, subject, of course, to Lady Catherine's conditions being fulfilled——

MRS. BENNET. On that score you may rest at ease.

COLLINS. As yet I cannot go further than to state that I am especially well satisfied with the appearance of Miss Jane, whose seniority gives her the prior claim.

MRS. BENNET. Ah, but Jane—as to my younger daughters I cannot take it upon me to say—I cannot positively answer—but I do not know of any prepossession. My eldest daughter—I feel it incumbent on me to hint—she is likely to be very soon engaged.

COLLINS. Ah ! In that case I must take note of the qualifications of Miss Elizabeth—second in seniority and perhaps in looks. I have the inside of a fortnight wherein to make my choice—and I am confident, madam, I shall not have to look beyond your family.

MRS. BENNET. I have five daughters, Mr. Collins.

COLLINS (*solemnly*). I cannot marry more than one.

CURTAIN.

ACT II

SCENE 1

(*The morning-room at Longbourn, eleven days later. The lawn handkerchief* ELIZABETH *was hemming in Act I is still in process of manufacture; it lies in her open work-basket on the table.*

From the conservatory CHARLOTTE *enters, ushered by* ELIZABETH, *who is in outdoor dress; she is just a little out of breath.*

ELIZABETH. Come in, Charlotte, come in! I spied you as you entered the gate!

CHARLOTTE. And ran to meet me! That was sweet of you! Mrs. Bennet is not yet dressed, I suppose? She must be very tired after the ball at Netherfield Park.

ELIZABETH. But happy in congratulating Jane! Within a fortnight of the momentous meeting amid the sheep, the stranger has been Jane's partner for two dances *and* supper at a ball in his own house! The affair does promise well, don't you think?

CHARLOTTE. First, where is everybody who was with you just now? From the top of the hill I descried you with Jane and Mr. Collins in the act of greeting Miss Bingley and her brother and his friend. What have you done with them all?

ELIZABETH. *I* did nothing but stand by forgotten, until there seemed to be a chance of attention from Mr. Bingley. I inquired his opinion of the weather. Deaf to my question, he sent his legs in the direction his eyes had already taken, in the wake of Jane. Whom Miss Bingley had pounced on and was leading away arm-in-arm. To view the hermitage.

CHARLOTTE. That left you with Mr. Collins and Mr. Darcy.

ELIZABETH. Oh, no! Mr. Darcy had walked off to the library, with a curious old book he had sent for from Pemberley to gloat over with papa. To his surprise and disgust he was escorted by Mr. Collins and under continuous bombardment of congratulations upon being the nephew of his aunt! For Mr. Collins had just received the honour of a letter from his patroness Lady Catherine de Bourgh, wherein she disclosed that the Mr. Darcy of Pemberley, mentioned in a letter of Mr. Collins to her, is her sister's son! In other words—freely provided by Mr. Collins to anyone who will listen—Mr. Darcy is the nephew of Lady Catherine de Bourgh; from which we may conclude that Lady Catherine de Bourgh is the aunt of Mr. Darcy!

CHARLOTTE (*laughing but with constraint*). Have you no pity for poor Mr. Collins? By now Mr. Darcy will have disappeared into the library, and the worthy clergyman——?

ELIZABETH. Must be searching the shrubberies for his fair cousin—who is thanking Heaven that to-morrow he must depart to his Lady Catherine and his valuable rectory. Why look so solemn, Charlotte? You have not yet wished me joy in the roseate prospects for Jane.

CHARLOTTE. To be honest, I cannot share your confidence. My chief purpose in coming to-day is to voice my uneasiness.

ELIZABETH. Oh? Though you yourself were witness that Bingley fell over head and ears in love at first sight?!

CHARLOTTE. Eagerness to fall in love is no proof of stability of character.

ELIZABETH (*with a wry mouth*). Eagerness—or even readiness —to fall is rather a proof of *instability*, you would say?

CHARLOTTE. I am never witty except by accident. All I have to offer is sober common sense on a dangerous situation.

ELIZABETH (*abashed*). You alarm me, Charlotte! Please go on!

CHARLOTTE. Before now you have remarked to me that Miss Bingley has a very firm hold on the reins at Netherfield Park. With her brother's most willing consent. He has grown up under her influence, and he seems to like yielding to Mr. Darcy as much as Mr. Darcy likes to guide and dominate him.

ELIZABETH. Oh, of course the friend of Mr. Darcy must marry wealth and rank as he himself is certain to. But Miss Bingley professes a gushing affection for Jane.

CHARLOTTE. She is false. Last night at supper I kept an eye on her whisperings to Mr. Darcy, which were plainly directed towards urging him to keep an eye on the lovers. I was quite shocked by the spitefulness of her smile, and the ruthless contempt in his sneer.

ELIZABETH. So her fancy for Jane is merely an excuse for playing gooseberry? But it leads her to give pressing invitations.

CHARLOTTE. Thereby depriving her brother's courtship of the interest of difficulty while preventing the lovers from being alone together.

ELIZABETH. Can any woman be guilty of such treachery?

CHARLOTTE. It gives her also the intimacy of a secret understanding with the man she herself is pursuing.—I *am* right in observing that Miss Bingley is pursuing Mr. Darcy?

ELIZABETH (*answering the casual question as casually*). Oh yes! Nearly every day he takes refuge here with papa.—How are we to combat this intrigue, Charlotte? To warn Jane would be worse than useless. She is too guileless to believe in an evil motive for anyone's behaviour.

CHARLOTTE. After all—and this Jane may believe—she is her own worst enemy.

ELIZABETH. How so?

CHARLOTTE. Her manner to Bingley is much too tranquil and composed. If she is to bring him to the point she must help him on.

ELIZABETH. She does help him on as much as her nature will allow. I greatly admire the way she guards her increasing love from general observation.

CHARLOTTE. But in so doing she hides it from her admirer. Such reserve may be fatal to the growth of his fancy. It is when a man knows himself beloved that his gratitude and vanity come into play. Without those aids to attachment, few lovers have heart enough to be fixedly in love.

ELIZABETH. As yet Jane cannot be certain how much she cares for Bingley.

CHARLOTTE. Then she should show more than she feels. When she is sure of him will be time enough for falling in love herself as deep as she chooses.

ELIZABETH. Jane does not act by design. To a mind like hers it would be rather indelicate for a courtship to reach its climax in less than five or six weeks. She must be allowed more than a fortnight to get to know her lover's character before she begins to commit herself.

CHARLOTTE. Oh, if she married him to-morrow her chance of happiness would be as good as if she studied his character for a twelvemonth. Indeed, it is better to know as little as possible of the defects of the person with whom one is to pass one's life.

ELIZABETH. You make me laugh, Charlotte. But it is not sound. You would never act in that way yourself.

CHARLOTTE. I am not romantic, you know. I never was, and have no desire to be.

(LYDIA *and* KITTY *burst in from the passage, in out-door costume.*)

LYDIA. Where did I leave " The Mysteries of Udolpho " ? Good morning, Miss Lucas !

KITTY. Good morning ! We are going to Meryton Library to change our novels.

(CHARLOTTE *has responded to the greetings.*)

ELIZABETH. You change your novels nearly every day.

KITTY. There are nearly always two or three officers in the library.

LYDIA. Pratt and Denny and Chamberlin said they'd be off duty this morning. Here's my book ! If we see Wickham, Lizzy, we'll give him your—best respects !—it doesn't do to be too forward at your age ! Come on, Kitty !

(*She dashes off, dragging* KITTY, *who joins her in loud laughter.*)

ELIZABETH. Lydia, your vulgarity—— She is unbearable !
CHARLOTTE. Mr. Wickham *is* paying you marked attention ?
ELIZABETH. No no, believe me !
CHARLOTTE. So stout a denial is enough to excite a wonder whether——

ELIZABETH (*interrupting*). The merest flirtation, based on a sympathy of dislike for Mr. Darcy. He has used Wickham shockingly !

CHARLOTTE. Oh ? !

ELIZABETH. Wickham was intended for the Church, and meant to take holy orders as soon as a certain living—a very good living—fell vacant. It was promised to him by the late Mr. Darcy, who was his godfather. But somehow the old gentleman muddled the matter in his will. So Mr. Fitzwilliam Darcy pretended there was no promise, and gave the appointment to another man !

CHARLOTTE. Abominable ! But what can have been his motive ?

ELIZABETH. Jealousy, I gathered. I shouldn't be surprised if the old gentleman preferred his godson to his son.

CHARLOTTE. The godson's manners are certainly more ingratiating. Was he very earnest to take holy orders ?

ELIZABETH. Oh no ! (*Without any ironic intent.*) He considers himself as well fitted for the Army as the Church. But the difference in income is enormous. Still, he doesn't complain. And for the sake of his godfather's memory he has never made the scandal public, and never will.

CHARLOTTE. He told you.

ELIZABETH. In confidence ! Perhaps I ought not to have passed it on even to you and Jane.

CHARLOTTE. It is safe with both of us . . . But, after all, you have no evidence but Wickham's word.

ELIZABETH. His word is ample. He is candour itself ! No one could mistrust him ! To me the very thought is impossible !

CHARLOTTE. Take care, Lizzy, take care !

ELIZABETH. The merest flirtation on both sides ! Anything else would be too imprudent. No, no, Mr. Collins is my only serious admirer. And my one wish concerning him is to keep out of his way. You have been angelic in helping me these last few days. Even to dancing with him twice last night. How your toes must have suffered ! He seems purposely to tread on his partner for the pleasure of apologizing.

CHARLOTTE. This morning I am the bearer of an invitation to him to dine with us and spend the evening.

ELIZABETH. Oh, I must kiss you for that ! How can you be so kind to such a creature ?

CHARLOTTE. I can't help being a little sorry for him. By the by, how did *you* manage to be so kind as to accept Mr. Darcy's hand for the first dance ? I was surprised to see him leading you out !

ELIZABETH. I was so amazed at his asking me that I heard myself accepting before I could think of a reason to say no.

CHARLOTTE. Why did he, I wonder ?

ELIZABETH. To annoy Miss Bingley, I suppose! Now shall we go and look for Mr. Collins and deliver your invitation?

CHARLOTTE. If we do that, my departure will leave you alone with him!

ELIZABETH. Oh dear, so it would! Is it too much to ask that you should seek him alone?

CHARLOTTE. I've no objection. Good-bye, dear!

ELIZABETH. Good-bye, best of friends!

CHARLOTTE (*turning at the conservatory door*). At my age one begins to grow tolerant of well-meaning people.

(*She goes out.*)

ELIZABETH (*alone*). Am I falling in love with Mr. Wickham? I wish I knew. I'm certainly falling deeper and deeper in hate with Mr. Fitzwilliam Darcy.

(*The door from the hall opens, and* DARCY *comes in, carrying an ancient chart and a magnifying glass.*)

DARCY. Oh, Miss Elizabeth!—I did not expect to find you alone—ah—Mr. Bennet sent me to enlist your help in deciphering a name on this ancient chart.

ELIZABETH. *My* help! How extraordinary of papa!

DARCY. Some acid seems to have been spilt on it. What do you make of the lettering down there?

ELIZABETH (*after looking*). Without the glass I can see nothing but a blur.

DARCY. With the glass then?

ELIZABETH (*after trying again*). I couldn't commit myself to any opinion. I have never attempted to solve such mysteries.

DARCY (*honestly disappointed*). I thought such very bright eyes would be exceptionally keen.

ELIZABETH. So it was *your* idea?—to lure me into making a fool of myself. (*She starts to hem industriously.*)

DARCY. Nothing of the sort, believe me! . . . Your hemming is exquisitely fine.

ELIZABETH. Indeed? You can see the stitches from that distance, although the letters of the chart defeated you?

DARCY. The last time I called here the handkerchief had fallen on the floor. You did not notice—I had the honour of picking it up.

ELIZABETH. Let me thank you now for your gallantry.

DARCY. I have heard my sister's governess tell her that the corners are the test of hemstitching.

(*He has advanced to the table. Laying down the glass, he tentatively holds out his hand.*)

ELIZABETH. How true!

DARCY (*after an awkward pause*). I suppose I had better give up wasting time on this puzzle. (*Looking at the chart.*)

ELIZABETH. Obviously consulting me has got you no further . . . Don't leave the magnifying-glass behind. You don't want to have to return for it.

(*He had started to go without it. He comes back, picks it up, hesitates, makes a fresh start, hesitates again, pulls himself together and strides off, after almost colliding with* MRS. BENNET.)

MRS. BENNET. Oh, Mr. Darcy ? How d'y' do ?

DARCY. Good morning, madam !

(*He goes out.*)

MRS. BENNET. What was he after ?—No matter. Just now from the dressing-room window I noticed Mr. Collins wandering about by himself. I want you to take him these cough-drops.

ELIZABETH. Oh, why ?—Mr. Collins hasn't got a cough.

MRS. BENNET. I noticed it at breakfast.

ELIZABETH. A crumb, because he was in such a hurry to apologize for upsetting my tea.

MRS. BENNET. Take him the cough-drops at once, miss ! Oh, here comes Jane with the Bingleys—how that girl does hang on to her brother !

(MISS BINGLEY *enters through the conservatory, followed by* JANE *and* BINGLEY. ELIZABETH *lingers.* MISS BINGLEY *is* " *a very fine lady* " *and* " *rather handsome . . . not deficient in good humour when she is pleased, but proud and conceited.*")

Ah, Miss Bingley, how pleased I am. . . . Will you sit here ? . . . Mr. Bingley—such a delightful dance at Netherfield last night. Jane, you ought to be getting on with your embroidery.

BINGLEY (*to* JANE). Sitting on that chair, you will like the frame higher, won't you ?

(*The embroidery-frame is under the window.* MRS. BENNET *has offered* MISS BINGLEY *a seat on the left end of the settee, and evidently means to sit at the other end herself. By this manœuvre* MISS BINGLEY *is unable to see what the lovers are doing, as her back is directly towards them.* MISS BINGLEY *sees the little trap, and changes to the other end of the settee, while* MRS. BENNET *is occupied with* ELIZABETH.)

ELIZABETH. Mr. Bingley, as soon as you have screwed the frame to the correct angle, would you be so good as to take these cough-drops to Mr. Collins ?

BINGLEY. With pleasure. (*Accepting the box.*) Where shall I find him ?

MRS. BENNET. Lizzy, I'm surprised at you ! I told you to go ! It's no matter who does the errand, of course, but I will not allow such independence ! Give the box back to her, if you please, Mr. Bingley !

(Bɪɴɢʟᴇʏ *obeys.*)

Eʟɪᴢᴀʙᴇᴛʜ. Very well, mamma !

(*She goes out through the conservatory.*)

Mʀs. Bᴇɴɴᴇᴛ (*coming down,* c.). Oh, Miss Bingley, you've moved ! I put you at this end for the sake of the cushion !

Mɪss Bɪɴɢʟᴇʏ. I wanted *you* to have the cushion, dear Mrs. Bennet ! I know how delicate you are !

Mʀs. Bᴇɴɴᴇᴛ. Oh, prodigious kind—nobody knows what I suffer—for all that—however !

Mɪss Bɪɴɢʟᴇʏ. Do come beside me, Mrs. Bennet !

(*The flustered* Mʀs. Bᴇɴɴᴇᴛ *now has her back to the lovers, and has to twist round whenever she feels she must observe them.*)

Mʀs. Bᴇɴɴᴇᴛ (*muttering*). Between one and another I don't know what to be at !

Bɪɴɢʟᴇʏ (*to* Jᴀɴᴇ). That is right now, I think ?

Jᴀɴᴇ. Perfectly, thank you.

(*The occupants of the settee bring their eyes back to each other.*)

Mɪss Bɪɴɢʟᴇʏ. Let me congratulate you, Mrs. Bennet, on the engagement that is so clearly foreshadowed !

Mʀs. Bᴇɴɴᴇᴛ. La, now, that's amiable ! I never reckoned on it you'd be so gratified !

Mɪss Bɪɴɢʟᴇʏ. The attentions last night at the ball were excessively marked !

Mʀs. Bᴇɴɴᴇᴛ. They were indeed ! It's a plain case of what Providence intended from the first.

Mɪss Bɪɴɢʟᴇʏ. I've already remarked to Jane, she will find it such an advantage to have a brother !

Mʀs. Bᴇɴɴᴇᴛ. A *what* ?

Mɪss Bɪɴɢʟᴇʏ. Brother-*in-law,* to be accurate ! Mr. Collins will be an excellent man to have in the family.

Mʀs. Bᴇɴɴᴇᴛ. It's Elizabeth he's after !

Mɪss Bɪɴɢʟᴇʏ. Of course !

Mʀs. Bᴇɴɴᴇᴛ. I warned him off Jane.

Mɪss Bɪɴɢʟᴇʏ. Did you ? Forgive me, but wasn't that rather unfair to the eldest daughter ? Jane is such a sweet creature ! It would be shocking if she didn't marry well, and it can hardly be expected that *two* portionless girls in one family will attract men of means and expectations.

Mʀs. Bᴇɴɴᴇᴛ. " Portionless " is no word to be using of a girl as lovely as Jane ! It's all most unfair—and how did you discover, any way ?

MISS BINGLEY. Lady Lucas was remarking that in the matter of fortune, her daughters are better off than yours.

MRS. BENNET. In the matter of looks they are ten thousand times worse ! Jane is *the* beauty of the whole county !

MISS BINGLEY. More admirable than her beauty is her cool good sense. She is the last woman in the world to mistake such philandering as Charles is indulging in now for more than it is worth !

MRS. BENNET. Mistake—oh, no indeed !

MISS BINGLEY. I laugh at Charles—always falling in and out of love ! Out more quickly than in ! But Jane is quite safe. It's as much of a game to her as it is to him.

MRS. BENNET. " Game ? " That's not the language I've taught my girls.

MISS BINGLEY. From a boy, Charles has been so much the ladies' man !

MRS. BENNETT. Oh, no doubt you knew him as a boy, which is more than I did—young men will be young men whatever we observe or don't observe——

MISS BINGLEY. I tell him he will end as an old bachelor—which will pay him out for his naughty ways !

MRS. BENNET. La, Miss Bingley, how can you say such a thing ? Though to be sure as long as he remains unwed you will have the ordering of his house, which must be pleasant enough at your age, and there's no certainty anything better will be offered you to the end of your days. Dear me, you shivered ! You're in a draught ! I'll move the screen to protect you—so.

(*The screen is either an unusually large pole fire-screen, measuring some two feet square, or a two-fold draught-screen on castors. In its new position it completely blocks* MISS BINGLEY'S *view of the lovers.*)

MISS BINGLEY. I don't feel any draught, I thank you.

JANE. I'm sorry to trouble you, Mr. Bingley, but there is a cross-light here ! Would you shift my frame over there ? (*To bring herself within the scope of* MISS BINGLEY'S *vision again.*)

MRS. BENNET. What nonsense, Jane ! It's a wonder you can never keep still for five minutes when you know how fidgeting frays my nerves !

MISS BINGLEY. How deliciously circumspect she is ! You didn't notice, dear Mrs. Bennet—by moving the screen to save me from draught, you isolated Jane and my brother. She won't have that ! She is determined to let him understand that *she* understands it is all make-believe and frivolity !

MRS. BENNET. Oh, however it may go, everybody is in league against me ! No one considers how ill I am or hesitates to use me atrociously !

MISS BINGLEY. Oh, my dear Mrs. Bennet——

(MARY *comes in from the hall, followed by* DARCY. *She is carrying a large book and bridling happily.*)

MRS. BENNET (*on the look-out for a victim*). Mary, what on earth are you doing with that book ? Didn't I say you were to walk into Meryton with Kitty and Lydia ?

MARY. No, ma'am—at least, I didn't hear you.

MRS. BENNET. Don't answer back. Read, read, read from morning to night, till your eyes look like burnt holes in a blanket and your shoulders are as round as a barrel.

JANE. Mamma dear !

MISS BINGLEY. Oughtn't Mrs. Bennet to lie down ? I fear she is more ill than she is aware.

MRS. BENNET. That is what I have always said. But those who never complain are never pitied. I don't want smelling-salts ! (*Pushing away the salts* JANE *offers.*) Only let me lean back and be quiet for two minutes. People who suffer as I do from nervous complaints have no great inclination for talking.— Put that book away, Mary !

MARY. Mr. Darcy has promised to write in it, ma'am ! My new album of *Elegant Extracts Penned by my Friends*, together with their signatures and the date.

DARCY. Miss Mary waylaid—met me, in the hall, and did me the honour to ask me for my favourite quotation and autograph.

MRS. BENNET. Why ever didn't you explain, Mary, when you came in ?

(MARY *arranges the book and the equipment she fetches from the writing-table, so that* DARCY *has his back to the left wall.* MISS BINGLEY *sits* C., *opposite to him.* MARY *sits at* DARCY'S *left elbow.*)

DARCY. Thank you.

MISS BINGLEY. Have you a ruler and pencil, Miss Mary ? Nobody could write straight on a page of that monstrous size without lines to help them.

DARCY. I can, I thank you.

MARY. I'll run for a ruler and pencil.

DARCY. Pray don't trouble ! I should not use them if they were here. (*He has chosen a quill, and now tries it on a sheet of loose paper.*)

MISS BINGLEY. How marvellous to write straight without lines ! At the finishing school I attended in London the writing master allowed us to rule lines whenever the page was large.

MRS. BENNET. My girls have had all the masters heart could wish, and I'd have sent them to a school if they'd expressed the desire.

MISS BINGLEY (*to* DARCY). Let me mend your pen for you. I mend pens remarkably well.

DARCY. Thank you—I always mend my own.

MISS BINGLEY. Have you a favourite quotation ready and certain ? Doubtless Miss Mary would fetch the book from the library.

DARCY. Quite unnecessary.

MISS BINGLEY. The grammar master often praised my memory for Shakespeare. But I could never write out a speech without looking at the book, for fear of the punctuation.

DARCY. The punctuation of Shakespeare is often a whim of the editor when it is not an error of the printer.

MISS BINGLEY. La, how learned you are !

MRS. BENNET. Mr. Bennet knows things about editors and printers compared to which Shakespeare is nothing at all.

MISS BINGLEY. How can you contrive to write so even ?

MRS. BENNET. Of my girls' handwritings, Mr. Darcy, Mary's is the evenest.

(DARCY *takes no notice of either of the last two remarks.*)

MISS BINGLEY (*deciding to turn from him*). Mr. Darcy writes the most charming letters to his sister.

DARCY. How do you know they are charming ?

MISS BINGLEY. I know they are long. It is a rule with me that length and charm in letters always go together. Every week Mr. Darcy writes to his sister. He is a model brother, and Georgiana is a charming girl. Lovely and highly accomplished. Charles, you once said Georgiana is the most charming girl you ever met.

BINGLEY. " The most charming *child* " I may have said. She was barely fifteen when I saw her.

MISS BINGLEY. She is sixteen now and almost ready to come out.

(DARCY *uses the pounce box.*)

MRS. BENNET (*sticking to her guns*). My Lydia is nearly sixteen and taller than any of the rest at her age.

MISS BINGLEY. Have you finished, Mr. Darcy ? You write uncommonly fast.

DARCY. You are mistaken. I write rather slowly.

MISS BINGLEY. I am dying to read your favourite extract !

DARCY. Miss Mary may prefer that the contents of her album should be private property.

MARY. Oh, how kind !—yes, thank you, I should !

MISS BINGLEY. To *my* album Mr. Darcy has contributed a water-colour sketch ! Trees and a shepherd and several cows— in exquisite taste !

DARCY. My drawings are those of a gentleman rather than an artist, I am afraid !

Miss Bingley.   I infinitely prefer them so!

(Elizabeth *returns*.)

Mrs. Bennet.   Well, Lizzy, has Mr. Collins gone to the library to speak to papa?

Elizabeth.   For all I know to the contrary, mamma.

Mrs. Bennet.   What—what?—the cough-drops still in your hand?

Elizabeth.   I couldn't find Mr. Collins, mamma!

Mrs. Bennet.   Oh, you tiresome, wilful girl! Upon my word, I'll——

Jane (*interrupting*).   If you please, mamma—Mr. Bingley has a request to make!

Mrs. Bennet.   Mr. Bingley, eh?

Bingley.   I am anxious to improve the conservatory at Netherfield. A visit to your greenhouses would put me on the right track.

Mrs. Bennet.   By all means! Jane will conduct you. She is the one for flowers.

Jane.   Mary, you will come too?—I am quite ignorant of the Latin names.

Mrs. Bennet.   'Tcha! Mr. Bingley doesn't want the Latin names.

Jane.   Gardeners and seedsmen recognize no others. Come, Mary!

Mary.   Do you really need me?

Darcy.   Perhaps *I* could be of use?

Mary.   I'm coming.

Miss Bingley.   Let us all go!

Darcy.   Miss Elizabeth, you will make one of the party?

Elizabeth.   I suppose so.

Mrs. Bennet.   No, you will not, miss! You will stay here with me! My nerves are in no state for solitude.

Elizabeth.   As you wish, mamma.

Miss Bingley (*the first to reach the door,* Bingley *has opened*). Why, here is Mr. Collins! At last the cough-drops can be delivered!

Elizabeth.   You will like to deliver them yourself, mamma!

Mrs. Bennet.   Impertinent hussy!

(*She thrusts aside the box* Elizabeth *offers.* Elizabeth *lays it on the table and makes for the passage-door. Meanwhile* Miss Bingley, Jane *and* Mary *have gone out through the conservatory, followed by the two young men.* Collins *reaches the threshold and pauses.*)

Collins.   Ah, there is my fair cousin!

Elizabeth.   I must take off my bonnet and cloak.

Mrs. Bennet.   Stay here—stay here, I tell you!

COLLINS. I beg your pardon, ladies, for this intrusion. I have just received an invitation from Miss Lucas to dine and spend the evening. At first I declined, but Miss Lucas amended the invitation to include my cousin, Miss Elizabeth. I ventured to accept for us both !

ELIZABETH. You had no right to ! I'm sorry, but I can't possibly——

MRS. BENNETT. What's to hinder you, stupid girl !—I accept for her, sir ! Stay here, Lizzy !

ELIZABETH. You stay too, dear madam !

MRS. BENNET. Mr. Collins has something to say to you ! I *insist* upon your hearing him. Take off your bonnet and cloak if you wish and sit down and listen.

(ELIZABETH *obeys and presently picks up her sewing.* MR. COLLINS *bows* MRS. BENNET *off. He remains on his feet, and presently arranges a chair with its back towards him, so that the top-rail serves as a pulpit-desk.*)

COLLINS. Believe me, my dear Miss Elizabeth, your modesty is far from doing you any disservice. You would have been less amiable in my eyes had there not been this little unwillingness. You can hardly doubt the purport of my discourse however your natural delicacy may lead you to dissemble. My attentions have been too marked to be mistaken. Almost as soon as I entered the house I singled you out as the companion of my future life.

ELIZABETH. Mr. Collins, I——

COLLINS. Allow me to continue.—(*clearly the speech has been prepared for delivery and memorized as if it were a sermon.*)—Before I am run away with by my feelings on this subject perhaps it would be advisable for me to state my reasons for marrying, and, moreover, for coming hither with the design of selecting a wife.

(ELIZABETH *has too much difficulty in controlling her laughter to check him at this point.*)

My reasons for marrying are, first, that I think it a right thing for every clergyman in easy circumstances (like myself) to set the example of matrimony in his parish ; secondly, that I am convinced it will add very greatly to my happiness ; and thirdly— which perhaps I ought to have mentioned earlier—that it is the particular advice and recommendation of the very noble lady whom I have the honour of calling patroness.

ELIZABETH. No reasons could be more—rational, sir, but——

COLLINS. One moment. In marrying my cousin I shall be making amends for the entail ; furthermore—this point occurred to me but just now—I shall be paying a delicate compliment to Mr. Fitzwilliam Darcy, who is shortly to be united in holy matrimony to *his* cousin, the daughter and sole heiress of Lady

Catherine de Bourgh. I have already mentioned the young lady to you.

ELIZABETH. You described Miss de Bourgh as sickly and plain.

COLLINS. Not " plain " ! I repeated Lady Catherine's own words : " possessing that *true* beauty which *plainly* marks her as of ancient descent."

ELIZABETH. I did not know Mr. Darcy was engaged to be married.

COLLINS. Her ladyship spoke of " an understanding "—and, of course in strict confidence.

ELIZABETH. Then you had no right to tell me !

COLLINS. My dear Miss Elizabeth, I intend to have no secrets from you !

ELIZABETH. What *you* intend——

COLLINS (*raising his voice*). I beg you will hear me out ! . . . Nothing now remains but to assure you of the violence of my affections. On the subject of your lack of fortune I shall be uniformly silent : no ungenerous reproach shall ever pass my lips when we are married.

ELIZABETH. You are too hasty, sir ! You forget that I have made no answer. Accept my thanks for the compliment you are paying me. I am very sensible of the honour of your proposals, but I cannot do otherwise than decline them.

COLLINS (*with a formal wave of his hand*). I am not now to learn that it is usual with young ladies to reject the addresses of the man they secretly mean to accept when he first applies for their favour, and that sometimes the refusal is repeated a second or even a third time.

ELIZABETH. Believe me, sir, I am not one of these young ladies—if such there be—who would risk their happiness so foolishly.

COLLINS. And believe me, I am by no means discouraged by what you have said and shall hope to lead you to the altar ere long.

ELIZABETH. Upon my word, sir, your hope is rather extraordinary after my declaration. You could not make *me* happy and I am the last woman in the world who could make *you* so. Nay, were your friend Lady Catherine to know me, I am persuaded she would find me in every respect unsuitable for the situation.

COLLINS (*very gravely*). Were it certain that Lady Catherine would think so—but no, your wit and vivacity must be acceptable to her, especially when tempered with the silence and respect her rank must inevitably excite. (*Intercepting her passage to the door.*) You have even now said as much to encourage my suit as would be consistent with the true delicacy of the female character.

ELIZABETH   really, Mr. Collins, you puzzle me exceedingly.

If what I have said can appear to you as encouragement, I know not how to express my refusal in such a way as to convince you.

COLLINS. My reasons for believing your rejection of my addresses to be merely words of course, are briefly these : the establishment I can offer, my position as rector, my prospects as heir to your father's estate, my connection with the family of de Bourgh—these are circumstances highly in my favour. On the other hand, and in spite of your numerous attractions, your lack of fortune deprives you of any certainty that another eligible offer of marriage will ever be made to you. I must therefore conclude that you are not serious in your rejection of me. You wish to increase my love by suspense according to the practice of elegant females.

ELIZABETH. I do assure you, sir, I have no pretensions to that kind of elegance. I thank you again and again for the honour you have done me. My feelings in every respect forbid me to accept you. Can I speak plainer ?

COLLINS. You are uniformly charming ! I am persuaded that when sanctioned by the approval of your father, the affair may be considered settled.

(ELIZABETH *makes for the door with such determination that he skips aside, leaving her to open it for herself.*)

MRS. BENNET (*off*). Lizzy, where are you going ? Let me come in.

ELIZABETH (*standing aside*). I am going to the library, ma'am, to speak to papa.

(MRS. BENNET *enters smiling.* ELIZABETH *is gone.*)

MRS. BENNET. O-oh ! (*Struck by a doubt.*) But it's for Mr. Collins, not you, to go to your father ! Lizzy !—Ah, well, it will make no difference in the long run. My dear sir, I wish you as happy as my darling girl can make you !

COLLINS. I thank you, dear madam. I am confident that I have chosen wisely and that I have every reason to be satisfied with my cousin's refusal.

MRS. BENNET. Refusal ?

COLLINS (*jauntily*). Again and again she vowed she would not accept me. But I am aware that these protestations did but express her bashful and timorous modesty.

MRS. BENNET (*startled*). That's not Lizzy ! I'm afraid she meant what she said, sir.

COLLINS (*thunderstruck*). Is it possible ?

MRS. BENNET. It'd be just like her ! But depend upon it she shall be brought to reason. I will speak to her myself directly. She is a very headstrong, foolish girl and does not know her own interest, but I will *make* her know it !

COLLINS (*intercepting her on her way to the door*). Pardon me for intercepting you, madam, but if she is really headstrong and foolish, I know not whether she would altogether be a very desirable wife.

Mrs. Bennet.   Sir, you quite misunderstand me.   Lizzy is only headstrong in such matters as these.   In everything else she is as good-natured a girl as ever lived.

Collins.   If Miss Elizabeth is liable to defects of temper, I am afraid she would not contribute much to my felicity.

Mrs. Bennet.   Now, now, Mr. Collins!   Leave Lizzy to me! I'll deal with her.

Collins.   Pardon me, madam——

Mrs. Bennet.   There, there, sir.—Do but step into the conservatory for a few minutes while I and Mr. Bennet have a word with her.

(*She almost pushes him into the conservatory, for* Elizabeth *is returning with* Mr. Bennet.)

Oh, Mr. Bennet, we are in such an uproar!   Has Lizzy told you the tale?

Mr. Bennet.   She begged me to come to the morning-room to explain some matter.

Mrs. Bennet.   Be quiet, Lizzy!   She has been vowing she will not have him, and if you do not make haste and insist that she does, he will change his mind and not have *her*.

Mr. Bennet (*blandly*).   Of whom are you talking, my dear?

Mrs. Bennet.   Of Mr. Collins and Lizzy, to be sure!   Lizzy declares she will not have Mr. Collins and Mr. Collins begins to say he will not have Lizzy.

Mr. Bennet.   And what am I to do?   It seems a hopeless business.

Mrs. Bennet.   Speak to her yourself.   Tell her that she must and shall.

(Elizabeth *has remained by the door into the hall*.)

Mr. Bennet.   Come here, child.   I understand that Mr. Collins has made you an offer of marriage?

Elizabeth.   Yes, papa.

Mr. Bennet.   Very well.   And this offer of marriage you have refused.

Elizabeth.   I have, sir.

Mr. Bennet.   Very well.   We now come to the point.   Your mother insists upon your accepting the offer.   Is it not so, Mrs. Bennet?

Mrs. Bennet.   Yes, or I will never speak to her again.

Mr. Bennet.   An unhappy alternative is before you, Elizabeth.   From this day you must be a stranger to one of your parents.   Your mother will never speak to you again if you do

not marry Mr. Collins, and I will never speak to you again if
you *do.*

ELIZABETH. Thank you, sir, thank you.

MRS. BENNET. Mr. Bennet, how can you disappoint me so ?
I am cruelly used indeed !

MR. BENNET. My dear, I have two small favours to ask.
First, that you will allow me the free use of my judgment on this
occasion. Second, that I may be permitted to return to my
library—(*going*)—and remain undisturbed.

(*He walks away into the hall, scarcely smiling back at* ELIZABETH
in response to her grateful glance and sigh of relief.)

MRS. BENNET. Oh ! Oh ! So the entail is to go on the same
as ever. No consideration for my poor nerves ! (*Spitefully.*)
I tell you what it is, Miss Lizzy, if you take it into your head to
refuse every offer of marriage, you will never get a husband at
all !

ELIZABETH (*waiting at the door until her mother has finished her
tirade*). I'm very sorry to vex you, ma'am.

(ELIZABETH *is gone into the hall.* MR. COLLINS, *who has been
watching for some three seconds, returns.*)

MRS. BENNET (*despairingly*). Oh, Mr. Collins !

COLLINS. My dear madam, I am resigned to my dismission.
Let us be for ever silent on this point. Far be it from me to
resent the conduct of your daughter. I am resigned. Not the
less so from a feeling of doubt as to my happiness had my fair
cousin honoured me with her hand. . . . I am now about to
retire to my room to compose my mind before dining with Sir
William Lucas. I think I may take it upon myself to convey
Miss Elizabeth's apologies for not accompanying me.

(MR. COLLINS *bows and goes into the hall.*)

MRS. BENNET. Oh ! Oh ! Oh !

(JANE *and* MARY *come in from the conservatory.*)

JANE. Is anything the matter, mamma ?

MRS. BENNET. Lizzy has refused Mr. Collins !—And her
father abets her naughtiness. You'll have to see what you can
do to persuade her.

JANE. No, ma'am. She alone can judge whether she loves
her admirer.

MRS. BENNET. " Loves " ? Who's to keep her when her
father dies ? I shan't have enough to keep myself.

(*A hubbub in the hall.*)

LYDIA.⎱Mamma ! Mamma ! Jane ! Lizzy !
KITTY.⎰

(LYDIA *and* KITTY *burst in.*)

LYDIA. Shocking news! We met Pratt and Denny on the road and turned back!

KITTY. Too horrible to be believed! The officers!

JANE. Hush! Hush!

MRS. BENNET. What is it? I cannot bear any more!

LYDIA. The regiment is ordered to Brighton.

KITTY. The regiment is ordered to Brighton.

(ELIZABETH *comes in.*)

ELIZABETH. Whatever's the matter?

HER FOUR SISTERS. The regiment is ordered to Brighton.

LYDIA. In three weeks' time!

KITTY. In three weeks' time!

ELIZABETH. Then you will have another three weeks of their society. Don't start crying before they are gone.

The CURTAIN *descends: the house-lights remain down. After a few seconds a tinkling instrument or drums and fifes play "The Girl I Left Behind Me." The tune dies away as the* CURTAIN *rises on* SCENE 2.

SCENE 2

The morning-room at Longbourn.
Three weeks later. Steady, quiet rain without.

Again the five MISSES BENNET *are present. This time* JANE *is sewing;* ELIZABETH *is reading a novel;* MARY *is writing;* KITTY *and* LYDIA, *seated close together on the settee, are crying assiduously.*

KITTY. We waved and waved till they were out of sight and the last sound died away.

LYDIA. Good Heaven, what is to become of us?

KITTY. If only the band hadn't played "The Girl I Left Behind Me."

LYDIA. Lizzy, you sit there smiling over a novel!

ELIZABETH. Why not?

LYDIA. The regiment is *gone*!

ELIZABETH. I'm not *trying* to be inconsolable.

MARY. Rational employment is the best defence of the mind against the griefs inseparable from mundane existence.

LYDIA. I can't make you out, Lizzy. You ought to be more wretched than us. Our beaus were only for flirting.

KITTY (*tearfully*). Such a crowd of beaus as we had!

LYDIA. Lizzy wanted to marry Wickham.

ELIZABETH. No, I did not. I can like a man and enjoy talking to him without wanting to marry him. . . . You are much too young to be thinking about marriage.

LYDIA. *You* aren't! If I were your age I'd have had Mr.

Collins. Mamma says neither you nor Jane take any pains to
get husbands. Jane will be quite an old maid soon, I declare.
She is almost three-and-twenty. Lord, how ashamed 1 should
be of not being married before three-and-twenty ! How I shall
laugh if I'm the first to wear a wedding-ring !

ELIZABETH. For goodness' sake think of something else !

LYDIA. Mrs. Forster was only a bit older than me when she
caught the Colonel last Christmas. She's the giddiest girl that
ever could be ! Oh, the laughs we've had together ! Did I tell
you, Lizzy, about how we dressed Chamberlin up in Mrs. Forster's
clothes, and presented him to a whole crowd of officers as the
Colonel's sister ?

ELIZABETH. You told me several times.

LYDIA (*undeterred*). And the whole crowd was quite taken in.
Only she and me burst out laughing and then Chamberlin let out
a great he-haw, so then they guessed the trick.

KITTY. And now all the fun is over for ever ! Oh, the
officers, the officers !

(LYDIA *echoes her sobs.*)

ELIZABETH. You've cried enough ! Get something to do !

LYDIA. There's nothing to do !

ELIZABETH. That rent in your ball-frock wants darning.

LYDIA. Ball-frock ! You are cruel !

KITTY (*singingly*). " And the girl I left behind me ! "

(*The pair fairly boo-hoo.* MRS. BENNET *comes in.*)

MRS. BENNET. Oh, my poor dear girls ! What a shame it is !
If only your father would be reasonable I'd take you to Brighton
for a month or two !

LYDIA. Papa is so unfeeling.

MRS. BENNET. A little sea-bathing would set me up for ever.

KITTY. And I'm sure it would do *me* a great deal of good.

(MR. BENNET *comes in from the hall with a letter in his hand.*)

MR. BENNET. Mrs. Bennet !—Sit down, children.—I have
received a letter by the post.

MRS. BENNET. Oh, Mr. Bennet ! How can you so harden
your heart ? Look at these poor girls' faces.

MR. BENNET. Their faces appear to need washing in cold
water.

MRS. BENNET. A month or two at Brighton would make all
the difference in the world to my nerves.

MR. BENNET. I shouldn't recognize you with different nerves,
my dear. Your return would be too embarrassing.

MRS. BENNET. As I've said before, the cost would be nothing
at all.

MR. BENNET.   Reiteration of a falsehood does not make it a truth.

JANE.   Papa, who is the letter from ?

MR. BENNET.   *Whom* is the letter from ?

JANE.   I beg pardon, sir—*whom* is the letter from ?

MR. BENNET.   Colonel Forster.   (*General interest is excited.*) To acknowledge my parting compliments.   (*He turns towards the door.*)

ELIZABETH.   Nothing else ?

MR. BENNET.   Oh—ah—yes.   (*Glancing at the letter.*)   He informs me that he will be very much occupied during the next three or four months, and his very young wife fears she will be very lonely.   (*Again he seems to be going.*)

MRS. BENNET.   Lonely ?   In Brighton Camp !

ELIZABETH.   Poor child !

JANE.   Is that all ?

MR. BENNET.   Let me see—no ; it's what I came in about. Colonel Forster concludes by saying it would be a charity if I would allow Lydia to keep his wife company.

MRS. BENNET.   What ?   Oh !   Oh !

LYDIA (*bouncing up*).   Keep Mrs. Forster company ?

MR. BENNET.   For three or four months, I understand.

LYDIA.   Oh, Heaven !

KITTY.   Only Lyddie ?

MRS. BENNET (*hugging* LYDIA).   Oh, my darling child !   How prodigiously delightful !

KITTY.   Why aren't I asked too ?

MRS. BENNET.   Don't be selfish, Kitty !

KITTY.   I've as much right to be asked—and more, for I'm two years older.

LYDIA.   Mrs. Forster likes me best !   She always did !   I laugh the loudest !   (*Capering and singing.*)   " So I am off to Brighton Camp, And ' you four are the girls ' I'll leave behind me ! "

(KITTY *sobs explosively.*)

MR. BENNET.   Stop that noise, Kitty !   (KITTY *does.*)   Will it console you if I refuse to let Lydia go ?

KITTY.   I don't see why she should if I can't !

MR. BENNET.   Do you know the story of the dog in the manger ?   I desire you will ponder the moral.

(KITTY *stands confused and irresolute.*   JANE *makes a sympathetic gesture,* KITTY *totters across, drops on the floor and smothers her sobs in* JANE'S *lap.*)

MRS. BENNET.   Dear Mr. Bennet, you must desire our youngest child to be happy !

MR. BENNET.   To deprive her of pleasure in order to gratify

Kitty would certainly be unjust. I must consider the matter.

LYDIA. Thank you, sir, thank you ! I know you'll give in to mamma if you say you will consider !

MRS. BENNET. Such a good father you have, girls ! Come, Lyddie, my love ! We must look through your wardrobe as quick as we can !

LYDIA. My ball-frock is torn—who'll mend it ?

MRS. BENNET. Mary shall ! Mary ! I want you upstairs, with your thimble. Jane, you come too. You can help me decide what Lyddie must have and what the rest of you must lend in the way of jewellery—fans—lace. Quick ! Quick ! Come along !

(She scurries out, followed by JANE *with* KITTY *clinging to her and* MARY.)

LYDIA. Lizzy, your corals—you will lend them to me !

ELIZABETH. Papa has not yet decided. You may not be going.

LYDIA. I am ! I am ! *(Running off, singing.)* " I am aw-aw-off to Brighton Camp, and I'll take your corals with me ! "

MR. BENNET. The house would be quieter without her.

*(*ELIZABETH *diffidently stops him as he starts to go.)*

ELIZABETH. If you please, sir—forgive me ! I can't help hoping you will put your foot down against this visit to Brighton.

MR. BENNET. There'd be endless complaint if I did. Why should I ?

ELIZABETH. Do you not often say that Lydia is extremely silly ? At home there are some checks on her wildness. At Brighton Camp it will be all dancing and flirting and playing practical jokes on the officers. Mrs. Forster is as flighty and boisterous as she is. Lydia will come back more unruly, more —I must say it—vulgar than ever.

MR. BENNET. Colonel Forster is a sensible man. He will keep her out of any real mischief. Luckily she is too poor to be an object of interest to any fortune-hunter. *(Going.)*

ELIZABETH. Papa dear, please, I greatly fear you take the matter too lightly. Bad manners in one sister disgrace the whole family.

MR. BENNET. T't, t't !

(While he is hesitating, the SERVANT *announces* MISS BINGLEY *and* MISS LUCAS.)

(To himself.) This incessant racket of women ! . . . Charmed to see you, ladies !

(Greetings and offering of chairs.)

MISS BINGLEY (*through the above*).   My carriage overtook Miss Lucas, and I prevailed on her to join me.

CHARLOTTE.   So kind !

(JANE *has run in.*)

JANE.   Mamma has sent me down to make her excuses. There is some possibility that Lydia may be paying a visit to Mrs. Forster.   It makes Mamma excessively busy.

MR. BENNET.   It makes me excessively busy also.   I must write at once to Colonel Forster.

ELIZABETH.   To accept the invitation, sir ?

JANE.   Oh, sir !   Is there such haste to decide—is she to go ?

MR. BENNET.   The house will be quieter without her.

(*He goes out.*)

ELIZABETH.   That means she has permission.

CHARLOTTE.   How delighted she must be !

MISS BINGLEY.   Dear Jane, you will sit by my side ?—I am paying a round of calls.—You know that on Tuesday last my brother and Mr. Darcy went up to London for a few days ?

JANE.   To stay until Saturday, I believe.

MISS BINGLEY.   That plan is cancelled.   Mr. Darcy has determined to open his town house in advance of the London Season.

JANE.   Then he will not be returning to Netherfield ?

MISS BINGLEY.   Oh, no !   He had already extended his visit from two weeks to more than five.—Do not ask me why ?

ELIZABETH.   So Mr. Bingley will come back alone ?

MISS BINGLEY.   Again, no !   Charles is to remain with Mr. Darcy.   I, too, am tired of the country, and have arranged to stay with my married sister in Mayfair.   Netherfield will be shut up.

CHARLOTTE (*the least concerned of her hearers*).   Not for very long, we shall all hope.

MISS BINGLEY.   Very likely until Charles has found a bride. Anyhow, until the shooting season.   Meanwhile we shall be mingling in really good society.   I am so particularly rejoiced that Mr. Darcy's household will include his sister Georgiana.

ELIZABETH.   With her governess ?

MISS BINGLEY.   No longer " governess "—" companion." Georgiana has celebrated her sixteenth birthday.   I love her devotedly, you know.   And my brother admires her excessively, as you must have heard him mention.   Dear Charles is singularly capable of winning the heart of a maiden who attracts him-- don't you think so, Jane ?

JANE.   Oh, yes !

ELIZABETH.   I believe, Miss Bingley, you call him a ladies' man, which to my mind is rather slighting.

MISS BINGLEY. I meant no disparagement. Provincial people are apt to misunderstand the phrases current in Mayfair —as also the gallant manner.

CHARLOTTE. Your married sister and Mr. Darcy both live in Mayfair, do they not ?

MISS BINGLEY. It is the fashionable quarter, you know.

ELIZABETH. Darcys and Bingleys will be like one family party. Vastly convenient—I mean, agreeable for you, so fond as you are of Miss Georgiana.

MISS BINGLEY. Dearest Jane, I must tear myself away ! This call was but *pour prendre congé.* My one regret in leaving this dull neighbourhood is parting from you. Come with me as far as the door and wave me farewell ! (*She exchanges curtsies with* CHARLOTTE *and* ELIZABETH *while talking to* JANE.) You must write to me often. I shall pine for letters.

(*She sweeps off, arm-in-arm with* JANE.)

ELIZABETH. What an appalling blow for poor Jane !

CHARLOTTE. I am very sorry.

ELIZABETH. The leading villain in the plot against her is Mr. Darcy. Did you notice ? He lured Bingley to town for a pretended " few days," and now holds him there. If I were a witch I'd punish Mr. Darcy ! I'd ill-wish him the worst wife in Christendom ! Which shall it be—the sickly, plain Miss de Bourgh or this false, insolent, spiteful Bingley woman.

CHARLOTTE (*dismissing the subject*). Does it matter ? . . . I've been longing for a quiet talk with you, Lizzy.

ELIZABETH. About Mr. Darcy ?

CHARLOTTE. No. Someone else. It is a little difficult to begin.

(MRS. BENNET *bustles in, talking.   She is dressed for the carriage.*)

MRS. BENNET. Lizzy ! I want you—— Oh, Charlotte still here ?—Good-morning-to-you-how-is-Lady-Lucas ? I've popped in to tell Lizzy I've ordered the carriage, to drive into Meryton for shopping for Lydia. If your papa comes out of the library I want you to tell him how pleased I am and what a good father he is, and I may have to spend more money than he might expect, but he may be very sure there'll be no extravagance.

ELIZABETH. I understand, ma'am.

MRS. BENNET. The other four girls are coming with me.

ELIZABETH. Not Jane ?

MRS. BENNET. Jane particularly. She is the only one who has the least notion what I shall like when it comes home from the shop.

ELIZABETH. I fear Jane has a headache, ma'am.

MRS. BENNET. A little shopping is the best thing in the world for a headache. And I'm in no fit state to argue with the younger ones. Mary has chosen to be as jealous as Kitty. I've had to promise to let them buy themselves presents at the milliner's. So you must do your best to persuade your father to be reasonable.

ELIZABETH. Mightn't I go with you instead of Jane ?

MRS. BENNET. No, you might not. You're no use to me in a shop, and Jane's no use for being witty with your father. . . . Good-day, Charlotte.

(MRS. BENNET *has gone.*)

ELIZABETH. Poor Jane ! She must be longing for a good cry !

CHARLOTTE. Yes, indeed ! Though I often tell you I am not romantic, I can sympathize.

ELIZABETH. You have news, have you not ?

CHARLOTTE. To romantic people it will sound rather tame.

ELIZABETH. You excite my curiosity.

CHARLOTTE. It begins with——

ELIZABETH. Well ?

CHARLOTTE. My father has had a letter from Mr. Collins, requesting an invitation to stay with us.

ELIZABETH. His dudgeon is too deep for him to want to come here again ! . . . But how hard on you ! . . . Charlotte !— Is Mr. Collins transferring his search for a wife to the Lucas family ? Oh, how funny !

CHARLOTTE. Why funny ?

ELIZABETH. Perhaps I should say, how melancholy ! *Do* you suspect him of amorous intention ?

CHARLOTTE. N-no.

ELIZABETH. You do !

CHARLOTTE. He and I are engaged to be married.

ELIZABETH. Engaged. My dear Charlotte ! Impossible !

CHARLOTTE (*regaining her composure after momentary confusion*). Why should you be surprised, my dear Elizabeth ?

ELIZABETH. Why ? Because—— I don't know.

CHARLOTTE. Do you think it incredible that Mr. Collins should succeed with any woman because he failed with you ?

ELIZABETH. I wish you all imaginable happiness, Charlotte !— I confess it never occurred to me.—You have been my special friend for many years ; it is highly gratifying that you will be my cousin by marriage.

CHARLOTTE. Thank you, dear—thank you. (*Bravely.*) I see what you are feeling. You *must* be surprised, very much surprised—so lately as Mr. Collins was wishing to marry you.

ELIZABETH. His motive then was a sense of duty—mis-guided, quixotic but rather noble. From a sense of duty he believed he cared for me. I could see he was self-deceived.

CHARLOTTE. He is most conscientious in all he does.

ELIZABETH (*after a pause*). You became engaged by letter, I suppose ?

CHARLOTTE. It was practically settled the evening he dined with us, three weeks ago. (*Bluntly honest.*) The very evening after your rejection of him.

ELIZABETH. How excellent that he was so quick to perceive his mistake ! . . . Is the wedding to be soon ?

CHARLOTTE. Quite soon, I believe.

ELIZABETH. I do hope you will be happy.

CHARLOTTE. I ask only a comfortable home. Considering Mr. Collins' character, connections and situation in life, I am convinced that my chance of happiness is as fair as most people can boast on entering the marriage state.

ELIZABETH. Undoubtedly.

CHARLOTTE (*after an awkward pause*). Lizzy, I have a favour to ask of you. Will you come and stay at the rectory ? Mr. Collins particularly said, he hoped you would stay with us. He is very forgiving.

ELIZABETH. What has he to forgive ? That I set him free to ask the woman he really wanted and who will make him an excellent wife ?

CHARLOTTE. My hope is that you will be our first guest after the honeymoon.

ELIZABETH (*stiffly*). I shall be happy to have the honour.

CHARLOTTE. Thank you ! Shall it be the month of May ?

ELIZABETH. With pleasure. May is a lovely month.

CHARLOTTE. I couldn't bear to lose your friendship. (*Rising.*)

ELIZABETH. Give Mr. Collins my sincere congratulations.

CHARLOTTE. I will indeed ! Thank you a thousand times ! Good-bye.

(CHARLOTTE *goes out by the conservatory.* ELIZABETH *drops into a chair.*)

ELIZABETH. How could she ? . . . The world is an uglier place than I have imagined.

(*She picks up her novel, turns the pages vaguely, and puts it down with emphasis.* The SERVANT *announces* MR. DARCY.)

DARCY. I find you alone ?

ELIZABETH. Everybody is out except my father. He will be pleased to see you. (*She moves towards the bell.*)

DARCY. Stay ! Do not ring, I beg. To find you alone is an unlooked-for piece of good fortune. I had hoped the weather would clear, and I might come upon you strolling in the park.

ELIZABETH (*after a pause*). Has Mr. Bingley returned with you ?

DARCY. No. He is unaware of my coming. I am going back to London to-night. . . . In vain have I struggled !—It will not do ! You must give me leave to tell you how ardently I admire and love you !

(ELIZABETH *is far too much astounded to be able to reply*.)

Almost from the first moment I saw you I had to fight against the amazing attraction you have for me. For the first two or three weeks I did not realize that my danger was serious. I have always taken for granted—it has been assumed in my upbringing —I think it is innate in me—to expect to marry in my own rank. A week ago I perceived that my one chance of safety lay in flight. I fancied that I had won—that I should never see you again— and here I am at your feet ! You cannot doubt the strength of my attachment.

ELIZABETH. *Attachment ?*

DARCY. My one anxiety now is lest I should fail to win your hand.

ELIZABETH. I don't believe you !

DARCY. You don't believe me ?

ELIZABETH. Your words expressed fear of failure, the tone was confident.

DARCY. I have been passing through agonies of self-combat.

ELIZABETH. By the rules of courtesy I should thank you. But I cannot. I feel no gratitude for sentiments so unwillingly yielded to. . . . I am sorry to have occasioned you the pain of self-combat. It was most unconsciously done on my part. . . . If you are hurt now by my refusal of your offer, the wound will soon heal.

DARCY (*after a pause*). And is this all the reply I am to expect ? Am I not even to be told why I am thus summarily rejected ?

ELIZABETH. I might as well inquire why you chose to inform me you liked me against your will, your training, your very nature. Could any approach be more insulting ?

DARCY. To insult you could obviously not be my aim.

ELIZABETH. You fancied *my* will, *my* nature to be such that I should not resent the insult. That is the grossest offence imaginable.

DARCY. Believe me—I am bewildered !—Perhaps I did under-rate the delicacy of your feelings. I am afraid I was engrossed in expressing my own. I am heartily sorry.

ELIZABETH. I have other provocations. You know I have. Is it likely I would accept a man who had plotted against the happiness of my best-loved sister ?

DARCY. I acknowledge that I set myself to do what I could to separate my friend from Miss Bennet. I hope I have succeeded.

ELIZABETH. With brutal disregard of her suffering !

DARCY. She will not suffer unduly. Though sweet, hers is a shallow nature.

ELIZABETH. How dare you presume to judge her ? I, who know her intimately, declare to you that her nature is deep and tender.

DARCY. You judge from your own. Which is unique. That is my justification.

ELIZABETH. Jane is my superior in every virtue, in every sensitiveness. She is as near perfection as mortal can be.

DARCY. Like you, she is self-controlled. Like you, she possesses manners and an air of breeding that would grace aristocratic birth. But I saw no indication that her heart was touched. I am confident Miss Bennet will not pine, though she would have married Bingley had the courtship developed.

ELIZABETH. You had no thought for his happiness ?

DARCY. Oh yes, I had. I was kinder to him than to myself.

ELIZABETH. Were you indeed ? How thankful you must be for my kindness in refusing you !

DARCY. You twist my meaning. But it would be false to deny that I foresaw discomfort from the inevitable family gatherings. Not only for my own sake. I have my sister Georgiana to consider. Can you wonder that I shrank from the thought of having to introduce Miss Lydia Bennet to her as the sister of my wife ?

ELIZABETH. For my feelings you neither had nor have the slightest consideration.

DARCY. On the contrary. I knew you would suffer likewise. For many years you must have suffered from the contrast between your own standards and those of everyone around you except Miss Jane. It was my dream to remove you from this unworthy environment to my ancestral home of Pemberley, where you would shine like a jewel in its true setting.

ELIZABETH. Delicious for me did I worship at your shrine of Pemberley ! Presumably your ancestors would approve of your " kindness " to Mr. Bingley. Would they also approve your conduct to Mr. Wickham ?

DARCY. Wickham ? What of that fellow ?

ELIZABETH. Yes, what of him ?—your father's godson, born and bred on your feudal estate.

DARCY. You take an eager interest in his affairs.

ELIZABETH. I asked whether it was in " the Pemberley tradition " to ruin a man with such claims upon you ?

DARCY. I ruin him ?—what slander has the scoundrel foisted on you ?

ELIZABETH. He had the promise of the best living in your father's gift. That promise you broke.

DARCY. There was no promise ! By my father's will the gift was in my discretion.

ELIZABETH.   So Mr. Wickham told me ! I have no respect for people who take advantage of the legal quibbles in wills.

DARCY.   You talk absurdly !—I beg your pardon—this you can understand—by the time the vacancy occurred Wickham's profligacy was such that I could not encourage him to become a clergyman.

ELIZABETH.   Oh, it is false ! You listened to malicious rumours. In your heart you must know that you acted meanly.

DARCY.   If anything I was over-generous. I gave him three thousand pounds to console him for the loss of expectations he himself had thrown away.

ELIZABETH.   All this is a fabrication !

DARCY.   Are you calling me a liar ?

ELIZABETH.   You spoke of profligacy—what had he done ?

DARCY.   I cannot tell you.

ELIZABETH.   I thought as much.

DARCY.   You shall hear of the final breach between us. When my sister was barely fifteen, he beguiled her into a scheme of elopement. At the last moment she could not endure the deception. She told me all. I sent him a letter. He left Derbyshire.

ELIZABETH.   Oh—a child ?—barely fifteen ?—I cannot believe it !

DARCY.   I can bring evidence. I have the acknowledgment of that three thousand pounds. The clause in my father's will is so simple, even a lady could not fail to comprehend it. But perhaps I stoop in vain. No proof of Wickham's villainy would alter your feelings towards me ?

ELIZABETH.   No proof of the whole world's villainy ! In the mode of your declaration you gave me proof enough of your own " ancestral " character.—If my words hardly make sense, it is because I have never in my life been so angry.

DARCY.   The truth is, your pride was hurt by my honesty. You would have preferred me to be blind to the ill-breeding continually displayed by your mother, your younger sisters—and occasionally by your father ! I can only say that my repugnance to connecting myself with your family was natural and just. Disguise of any sort is abhorrent to me.

ELIZABETH.   Very well ! I will be frank with you in return. From the beginning I was impressed by your arrogance, your conceit and your selfish disdain of others. I had not known you a week before I felt you were the last man in the world I could ever be prevailed upon to marry. I am glad that the manner of your proposal was offensive ; it has spared me the concern I might otherwise have felt in refusing you, had your behaviour been more gentlemanly.

DARCY.   You have said enough, madam. Forgive me for

having taken up so much of your time. (*He bows and strides to the door.*)   I have only to add, God bless you !

(*He goes out and shuts the door.*   ELIZABETH *bursts into tears, and cries and cries.*)

CURTAIN.

ACT III

The morning-room at Longbourn. Four months later. The July sun is bright. Summer curtains have replaced winter ones at the windows.

Four girls are present. JANE and ELIZABETH are plying their needles with an industry that betokens a resolute intention to overcome despondency. JANE has started on a new canvas in the embroidery frame. ELIZABETH is mending lace. MARY is reading. KITTY has a novel in her hand but is not reading. There is silence for two seconds. With a sudden movement JANE shifts her embroidery frame and sits gazing straight in front of her. ELIZABETH leans towards her as if to speak but decides not to. She resumes her work but almost instantly lets it drop into her lap. Listlessly MARY turns a page. A huge sigh from KITTY causes the other three to brace themselves for a renewal of their labours.

MRS. BENNET makes a languid entrance from the hall and lets herself sink into the chair JANE is quick to offer. She is clad in a voluminous wrapper and large frilled night-cap.

JANE. Oh, ma'am! Are you fit to be out of bed?

MRS. BENNET (*plaintively*). I'm not fit to be left alone for hours at a stretch. The only one who ever loved me was my poor dear Lyddie, and it's—oh, how many months since I've been without her? (*In shrill anger.*) Can none of you be at the trouble to tell me how many months since Lyddie went away to Brighton?

JANE. Four months, ma'am.

(The two youngest girls are trying to deafen themselves to their mother's maunderings by assiduous reading.)

MRS. BENNET. I'm sure it must be five. . . . Mary! Kitty! Haven't you sufficient pity for my nerves to spare me the sight of *reading?*—If you must bury yourselves in books, take them out into the park!

(Reluctantly MARY and KITTY rise to obey. MARY collects paper and pencil, and methodically puts a marker in her book. KITTY dog's-ears her place.)

KITTY (*fretfully*). It's so prodigious hot!

MRS. BENNET. You can sit in the shade. . . . Don't slouch so! Don't forget your parasols! And for Heaven's sake don't show me your faces again until you can look more agreeable!

(The parasols of the family stand in a big Chinese jar close to the door into the conservatory.

On hearing the SERVANT announce MR. COLLINS, MARY and

Kɪᴛᴛʏ *bolt out through the conservatory. With equal promptness*
Eʟɪᴢᴀʙᴇᴛʜ *hastens to prevent* Mʀ. Cᴏʟʟɪɴs's *entrance.*)

Eʟɪᴢᴀʙᴇᴛʜ. Oh, sir, you must excuse the mistake—mamma
is not receiving callers to-day !

Sᴇʀᴠᴀɴᴛ. I thought the mistress was upstairs, m'm. (*N.B.
not* " miss ".)

Mʀs. Bᴇɴɴᴇᴛ (*calling out*). Come in, Mr. Collins ! I'm not
dressed, but a clergyman doesn't signify. Pray come in !

Cᴏʟʟɪɴs (*appearing, with a deep bow*). Permit me to apologize
—I am come to condole with you on your grievous affliction.

Mʀs. Bᴇɴɴᴇᴛ. Grievous indeed ! I get no sleep at all.
Twice over last night I had to call Jane to try if a little chat
would help me to drop off, but it only seemed to make me the
more wakeful.

(*During the above speech* Mʀ. Cᴏʟʟɪɴs *has distributed a polite bow
to* Jᴀɴᴇ *and a severe one to* Eʟɪᴢᴀʙᴇᴛʜ, *and received curtsies
in exchange.*)

Eʟɪᴢᴀʙᴇᴛʜ. How did you leave Charlotte, Mr. Collins ?

Cᴏʟʟɪɴs. In very good health, I thank you.

Mʀs. Bᴇɴɴᴇᴛ. Pray be seated, sir.

(*She does not ask him to put down his hat, so he must cling to it.*)

Cᴏʟʟɪɴs. I thank you. . . . Let me without delay assure
you, Mrs. Bennet, that my dear wife joins me in sincerest sympathy for the loss of your youngest daughter.

Mʀs. Bᴇɴɴᴇᴛ. 'Sakes ha' mercy ! She's not dead !

Cᴏʟʟɪɴs. Death would have been a blessing in comparison
with infamy.

Mʀs. Bᴇɴɴᴇᴛ. Fiddle-dee-dee ! She has but run off with an
officer to Gretna Green !

Jᴀɴᴇ. She left a note for Mrs. Forster to say they were going
to Gretna Green.

Cᴏʟʟɪɴs. A fortnight has elapsed, yet nothing further has
been heard of them.

Mʀs. Bᴇɴɴᴇᴛ. Yes, there has ! Mr. Bennet traced them to
Clapham, and there they changed into a hackney cab.

Cᴏʟʟɪɴs. A hackney cab would not convey them beyond
London.

Mʀs. Bᴇɴɴᴇᴛ. I've said all along, it's cheaper to get married
in London, though it does take three weeks.

Jᴀɴᴇ. We must be patient for another few days.

Mʀs. Bᴇɴɴᴇᴛ. My poor, dear Lyddie ! If I had been able
to carry my point in going to Brighton, this would never have
happened. She is not the kind of girl to do such a thing if she
had been well looked after. I always thought the Forsters were
very unfit to have the charge of her, but I was overruled, as I
always am.

COLLINS. From Sir William Lucas's account I gathered that the poverty of the fugitives is no less deplorable than their morals. Mr. Wickham was in flight from his creditors.

MRS. BENNET. Whoever would have thought it of Wickham ? —Such a handsome man !

JANE. Everybody in Meryton thought well of him.

MRS. BENNET. What's very odd and surprising—when he used to come here, it wasn't with Lyddie he flirted. It was (*pointing to* ELIZABETH) that young lady I had to keep on reminding she couldn't live on his pay.

ELIZABETH. Oh, ma'am !

COLLINS. Just so. Charlotte was of opinion that Miss Elizabeth's predilection for an unworthy admirer was the true cause of her refusal of a certain suitor whom you and I, Mrs. Bennet, regarded as perfectly eligible.

ELIZABETH. No, no, Mr. Collins ! I refused you on your own merits, believe me ! As for Mr. Wickham—I told Charlotte, two months ago, I was surprised to find how completely my interest in him had faded away.

MRS. BENNET. Lizzy did pay heed to me in the matter of Wickham, Mr. Collins—I'll say that for her. Though she hadn't the sense to take you.

COLLINS. Miss Elizabeth is well aware that I proposed to her from a compulsion of duty. Her refusal was a relief to me, and I am now settled with one who affords me the utmost matrimonial felicity—some part cf which Miss Elizabeth has witnessed for herself in the course of the visit wherewith she honoured us.

ELIZABETH. I did indeed ! Charlotte and you are admirably suited.

COLLINS. Now my satisfaction is augmented by thankfulness that I have no closer connection with the Bennet family than that of cousin, and am not involved in its disgrace.

MRS. BENNET. What's that you are saying ?

JANE. Elizabeth greatly enjoyed her stay at the Rectory, Mr. Collins.

COLLINS. As guest at the Rectory, Miss Elizabeth was included in every invitation we received from Lady Catherine de Bourgh, who extended to her all that affability and condescension which is habitual in her ladyship's manner to Charlotte and myself.

ELIZABETH. Her ladyship's condescension was an amazing experience.

MRS. BENNET. Oh, so long as you can gad about to rectories, and dine and play cards with Lady Catherines—and all such grandeur and gaiety, it's little you care for my torments and anxiety for the fate of my darling Lydia !—Oh, Mr. Collins, such a fit of hysterics as I had when Mr. Bennet got Colonel Forster's letter, and rushed off on Lyddie's track ! Such a taking Mr.

Bennet was in !—Jane was quite frightened ! (*She pauses for breath.*)

JANE. I never saw my father so angry.

MRS. BENNET (*continuing*). I *knew* he'd fight Wickham and be killed, and you and Charlotte would turn us out of house and home before he was cold in his grave !

COLLINS (*solemnly*). Not so, Mrs. Bennet, I assure you ! Charlotte and I are at one in the decision to allow you an ample margin of time for your removal when your widowhood does befall as ordained.

MRS. BENNET (*with a snort*). It's not so bound-to-be as all that ! Mr. Bennet may live to be eighty, and younger men than you have died of a fever or a fall from a horse. If you weren't a clergyman, you're the right age to challenge Wickham and have a bullet put into you. Or put one into him and set matters right. As it is, you're no use at all, and there's no one to shoot Wickham. For Mr. Bennet came back to us three nights ago. He has given up the chase.

COLLINS. I trust he is resigned to leaving his lost daughter to reap the fruits of her heinous offence.

JANE. Oh, no, no ! Papa is still deeply distressed. But he has now put the affair into the hands of our uncle in Gracechurch Street. He is a capable business man and knows the ways of the world and what is best to be done.

MRS. BENNET. Very true, my dear. And all will be well if my good brother does but remember the message I wrote him for Lyddie when he discovers her. She is not to wait for wedding-clothes. For she can have as much money as she chooses to buy them after she is married. Furthermore, she is not to linger in town to give any directions for the clothes, but to come straight here, and I will tell her the best warehouses.

COLLINS. Mrs. Bennet, you amaze me ! Are you proposing to treat the erring one as though a marriage ceremony could undo the past ?

MRS. BENNET. Good Lord, whyever not ? They must needs go to church, but who cares if it was the morning before—or a week or two after—— ? The parson gets his fee.

COLLINS. I must speak to Mr. Bennet ! He ought certainly to forgive the sinner as a Christian, but never to see her again or allow her name to be mentioned in his presence.

MRS. BENNET. Oh ! Oh !

COLLINS. Consider, my dear Mrs. Bennet, consider ! For the sake of your respectable daughters, the disreputable cne must be cast out.

(MRS. BENNET *splutters with wrath.*)

JANE (*with unwonted spirit*). If Lydia repents, none of us could desire that she should be unkindly treated for our sakes.

Mrs. Bennet. If they did, they'd deserve to be whipped at the cart's tail.

Collins (*rising*). I decline to remain a part to such an immoral conversation.

(Kitty *runs in from the conservatory*.)

Kitty. Mamma! News! News! I've just had a word with the butcher's boy!

Mrs. Bennet. News of my Lyddie?

Kitty. No! . . . Mr. Bingley is back at Netherfield!

(Mr. Collins *lingers; he wants to hear more*.)

Mrs. Bennet. Bingley back at Netherfield? Oh, vastly cheering!

Kitty. He returned yesterday. But whether he sent any warning to the housekeeper or turned up unexpectedly, the butcher's boy couldn't say.

Mrs. Bennet. I must go and dress.

Jane. You are not well enough to dress, dear madam!

Mrs. Bennet. Stop ordering me about! There's no telling who may call. (*She rings the bell*.)

Elizabeth. Surely you wish to be denied to every caller—at least until Lydia is found!

Jane. I couldn't bear it, ma'am——

Collins. Let me add the full weight of my counsel : remain secluded!

(*The* Servant *appears*.)

Mrs. Bennet. I am about to dress, and shall be receiving this morning as usual.

Servant. Very good, madam.

Mrs. Bennet. Kitty, I'd like you to help me. (*Talking herself off, after the slightest possible curtsy to* Collins.) Was there any more news to be got from the butcher's boy?

Kitty. I didn't wait for any more.

(Kitty *follows* Mrs. Bennet *off*.)

Collins (*seating himself again, in great consternation*). I cannot imagine what Lady Catherine would say to this lightmindedness!

Elizabeth. Why try to imagine? She is not concerned.

Collins. You mistake! Her ladyship expressed very great concern. Especially for the effect of the scandal on the fortunes of the remaining daughters.

Elizabeth. Did you betray our family secret to Lady Catherine de Bourgh?

Collins. No secret! The information reached me in a letter from Sir William Lucas. It is not the sort of thing Lady Catherine likes to be kept from her knowledge. Nor is she slow to offer the best advice.   In this case she condescended to hope that Mr. and Mrs. Bennet would be wise enough to withdraw from county society, and seek new acquaintances in a lower sphere. " For what man of position," she justly observed, " will pay honourable attentions to any female of such a family ? "   I think I should add, Miss Elizabeth, that this conversation occurred while her ladyship was shuffling the cards for a game of back-gammon with Mr. Darcy.

JANE.   Mr. Darcy ?

ELIZABETH (*courageously, though with an effort*).   And what did he say ?

COLLINS.   Nothing !   Not one syllable.   With a rudeness Lady Catherine had never previously encountered, Mr. Darcy arose from the table and silently walked out of the room ! " Gracious heavens ! " exclaimed her ladyship, " Whatever possesses him ? "   Most unfortunately Miss de Bourgh's com-panion was moved to remark that Mr. Darcy's last visit to his aunt was coincident with the latter part of the visit to the rectory of another of the Miss Bennets.

JANE.   Why was the remark unfortunate ?

COLLINS.   Let me proceed !   On that occasion Mr. Darcy was self-invited, and he stayed three weeks instead of his customary two days.   Until that moment these facts had been connected in her ladyship's mind with nothing but Mr. Darcy's courtship of Miss de Bourgh.

ELIZABETH.   More than once I have heard both you and the companion congratulate her ladyship on these proofs of his intentions.

COLLINS.   Imagine my consternation !   Those graceful little compliments suddenly appeared to her ladyship in the light of dust thrown in her eyes !   She actually accused me of complicity in a design too monstrous for me to put into words.   The best Charlotte and I together could do was to promise that the offence shall never be repeated.   Miss Elizabeth shall receive no second invitation.

ELIZABETH.   Does etiquette demand that I thank you—or should I apologize ? . . .   Lady Catherine's next step, I suppose, was to ask Mr. Darcy what his intentions actually are ?

COLLINS.   Allow me to continue my narrative.   In spite of all we could say, her ladyship was by no means tranquillized, when the butler appeared with a message from Mr. Darcy of regret that he had suddenly been called away on important business. No clue to that business transpired except that he had taken the London road and was whipping his horse to a gallop.

JANE.   Mr. Collins, nothing of all this about Lady Catherine and her advice and the rest can be of the least use to mamma or papa.   I do beg you will keep it from them and avoid hurting their feelings unnecessarily.

COLLINS. In effect you repeat what Charlotte urged upon me, with respect to your whole family. I shall have to explain to her that—er—my cousins questioned me and I—er—forgot the caution she enjoined. In talk with Mrs. Bennet, however, I said nothing for which I can reproach myself. Mr. Bennet, I understand, has gone out for a walk.

JANE. I do not know when he will be back.

ELIZABETH. In the meantime, Mr. Collins, you will like a little turn in the park ? You will prefer to be alone.

COLLINS. The opportunity to collect my thoughts is by no means unwelcome. I will therefore withdraw.

(*He speaks huffily, bows twice and departs through the conservatory.* JANE *melts into tears.*)

ELIZABETH. Jane ! Oh, my dearest, sweetest !—if you give way, what shall I do ?

JANE. It is nothing. I am a little over-tired with sitting up at night with mamma.

ELIZABETH. The situation is too cruel. Bingley back at Netherfield, and our one prayer that he will not call !

JANE. I am not really crying. I would not be so foolish.

ELIZABETH. That wretched, wretched Lydia !

JANE. Do not blame her for *my* trouble. That dates from the spring when Bingley broke away.

ELIZABETH. His abominable, scheming sister ! Why, oh why had he so little determination in courting you ?

JANE. The answer is simple : his attentions did not amount to courtship. He did not love me. Perhaps he withdrew because he had some suspicion of my feeling for him. I have nothing to reproach him with. Thank God, I have not that pain.

ELIZABETH. If he does call—— ?

JANE. I must meet him coldly. For his sake now I must avoid his company. At any rate unless or until Lydia marries. Eventually we may be friendly again, but for me romance is at an end. How thankful I am, dear Lizzy, that you are not suffering likewise. You did see a good deal of Mr. Darcy—you told me—when you were with the Collinses. Had you cared for him, I should have your disappointment to bear as well as my own.

ELIZABETH. Oh, Jane, Jane ! (*She melts into tears.*)

JANE. Why, Lizzy, you had refused him ! You dislike him intensely !

ELIZABETH (*wailing*). My feelings have changed ! His manner to me recently—every time we met—all he said and did was everything one could desire.

JANE. Were you actually beginning to look forward to a second proposal ?

ELIZABETH. I'm afraid I was.

JANE. And he—did he make clear—— ?

ELIZABETH. Hardly that. But he did appear to be taking
some pains to win my approval. Or so I imagined.

JANE. I wonder what made him go dashing off to London
when he heard about Lydia ?

ELIZABETH. Don't set *me* wondering ! . . . Whatever hap-
pens I must abandon all hope of happiness now. Wickham for
a brother-in-law would be almost more insupportable to a Darcy's
pride than Lydia for an ought-to-be-married sister-in-law.

JANE. Suppose Mr. Darcy revisits Netherfield ! Your situation will be infinitely more painful than mine.

ELIZABETH. What I must endure is fair punishment for my
prejudice.

JANE. It is something that you and I are in fullest sympathy.

ELIZABETH (*putting her arms round* JANE'S *neck*). The first
wish of both our hearts is never again to be in the company of the
men we love.

(*They embrace tearfully.*

MR. BENNET *comes in from the hall, hat in hand, intending to
go out through the conservatory after a word with the ladies.*)

JANE. Oh, sir——

ELIZABETH. You have been for the post ?—Was there any
letter ?

MR. BENNET (*harassed and dejected*). No.

ELIZABETH. Papa dear !—We are so grieved for your share
of the suffering.

MR. BENNET. Say nothing of that. It has been my own
doing, and I ought to suffer.

ELIZABETH. You must not be too severe upon yourself.

MR. BENNET. You may well warn me against such an evil.
Human nature is so prone to fall into it. No, Lizzy, let me once
in my life feel how much I have been to blame. I am not afraid
of being overpowered by the impression. It will pass away soon
enough. . . . By the by, my dear, I bear you no ill-will for being
justified in your advice to me last March—which, considering the
event, shows some greatness of mind.

ELIZABETH (*putting an affectionate hand on his arm*). My dear
father !

JANE. You will like to know, sir, that mamma is equal to
dressing.

MR. BENNET. I have lost an opportunity by not making a
similar parade of undress. Next time a daughter runs away
I shall sit in my library in my night-cap and powdering-gown, and
give as much trouble as I can. . . . This time, being dressed
even to my boots, I may as well vent my righteous indignation
against myself upon my gamekeeper. (*Moving towards the conservatory.*) No doubt he has been as negligent in preserving the

pheasants on the estate as I in preserving the young women.

ELIZABETH (*intercepting him*). Papa! Mr. Collins is in the park!

JANE.   He is anxious to talk with you!

MR. BENNET.   Heaven preserve me!

ELIZABETH.   He is coming this way!

MR. BENNET.   Tell him of my intention to inspect my coverts. Tell him ho may seek me in the Far Spinney. Anywhere but in the library!

(*He bolts into the hall.*)

ELIZABETH.   If a fib is necessary, leave it to me, Jane! My conscience is tougher than yours.

JANE.   My brain is unequal to *evading* a falsehood. (*With unqualified admiration.*)   At need you do it so cleverly.

(COLLINS *reappears. After bowing he mops his brow.*)

COLLINS.   I apologize, ladies, for this reintrusion. Can you, Miss Jane, inform me in which direction Mr. Bennet has gone?

JANE.   Elizabeth can, I believe.

ELIZABETH.   If I understood my father aright, the place to seek him is the Far Spinney. I know he meant to go the round of the coverts. When he does that, he returns over the hill and by the farm. You could not mistake the path if you went to meet him.

COLLINS.   The sun is too hot for walking to be wholesome. With your permission, ladies, I will sit, till Mr. Bennet returns, in your company. If you will resume your needlework, I shall be happy to read aloud to you. When I was here in the spring, I began to read aloud one of Fordyce's Sermons. Did you finish it by yourselves?

JANE.   }No.   Didn't we, Jane?   Anyhow it makes no
ELIZABETH.}Yes.
difference what Mr. Collins reads aloud. The volume is kept in the morning-room because of its weight; it is excellent for pressing lace.

(*She hands him the volume.*   MRS. BENNET *returns.*)

MRS. BENNET.   Jane! Lizzy! I feel a new woman now I'm dressed.   Oh, Mr. Collins! Still hanging about?

COLLINS.   I was on the point, madam, of——

MRS. BENNET.   No, no, for mercy's sake! My nerves will not stand being read to! The mere sight of a book puts me in a fidget.

COLLINS.   Very well, madam, as my presence among the ladies is not gratifying to them—it could not be inconvenient for me to await Mr. Bennet's return in the library.

MRS. BENNET.   Mr. Bennet has no liking for gentlemen awaiting him in the library. If it's more bad language about my Lyddie you are concocting in your head, it'd be much more becoming in you to mind your own business and hold your tongue.

COLLINS. Pardon me, Mrs. Bennet, to that restriction I cannot submit. A clergyman must speak. I am determined that no arguments shall be wanting on my part that can alleviate Mr. Bennet's misery. Charlotte herself was unable to dissuade me from the performance of this duty.

JANE. How is Charlotte, Mr. Collins ?

COLLINS. I thank you for the kind repetition of Miss Elizabeth's inquiry. My reply is limited by my promise to Charlotte to say no more than that her health is very good.

MRS. BENNET. Ho ? Morning sickness, I'll be bound ! (COLLINS bows.) Well, assure her from me she is not suffering half what I did with all my five. And if it turns out to be a girl, I shall be the last to pity her, for it's most unfair if I'm to be the only one to have my nerves frayed to a frazzle by that monstrous entail.

ELIZABETH. Pray, Mr. Collins, give Charlotte our best wishes !

JANE. Yes, indeed ! The best wishes of the whole family is the message you would like Mr. Collins to deliver, is it not, mamma ?

MRS. BENNET. That was my meaning. Everything right and proper is what I always desire.

COLLINS. In return I cannot too strongly express my thanks, my very sincere thanks.

MRS. BENNET. Be seated, sir, do ! You make me quite giddy, standing there bowing like a marionette !

COLLINS. Again I thank you. Lady Catherine de Bourgh has already informed herself of the truth and bestowed excellent advice.

MRS. BENNET. Humph ! By all accounts Lady Catherine is a mother to take warning by. Her output is but one sickly, plain, undersized shrew, not quite right in the head.

COLLINS. Mrs. Bennet !

ELIZABETH. Oh, mamma, you have exaggerated my description !

(*The* SERVANT *enters.*)

SERVANT. If you please, ma'am, a lady to see you, and I am not to announce the name.

LYDIA (*off*). Tantivy ! Tantivy !

(*She rushes in, shouting,*)

A view ! A view ! (*Sweeping a deep curtsy.*) Mrs. Wickham ! Who is the first to wear a wedding-ring ? The youngest !

(KITTY *runs in, followed after a moment by* MARY.)

What do you think of me, Lizzy, running off with the man you were after ? Oh, I shall split with laughing !

MRS. BENNET (*embracing her and speaking through the latter part of her speech*). My dear, dear darling ! So all is well ! Married ! At sixteen ! I knew how it would be ! Delicious fun !

LYDIA. Let go of me, mamma ! Give the others their turn to wish me joy !

ELIZABETH. I'm extremely glad you are married.

JANE. I trust you and your husband will be happy——

MARY. In so far as happiness is possible in the circumstances you have created.

KITTY (*beginning before MARY has finished*). I'm monstrous glad ! We've had a miserable time.

LYDIA (*grandly, with a minuet gesture*). The bride returns her thanks !—La, Mr. Collins, how you stand there, stuck and dumb !

COLLINS. Speech fails me, madam !

LYDIA. The London parson who did the wedding—he claimed his privilege to kiss the bride. (*Dancing up to him, she presents her cheek.*)

COLLINS (*backing*). I have the honour to wish you all, Good morning ! . . . (*As a parting shot.*) I do not encourage vice !

(*He departs through the conservatory.*)

LYDIA. Good Lord, isn't he disagreeable ?

(KITTY *giggles.*)

MRS. BENNET. Odious man ! . . . But where, oh, where is dear Wickham ? Is he not with you ?

LYDIA (*pouting a little*). He declared he'd sooner wait at the inn.

MRS. BENNET. Whatever for ?

LYDIA. To know papa's pleasure.

MRS. BENNET. 'Tcha ! What should be his pleasure but a warm welcome.

ELIZABETH. Papa is in the library ! Go to him at once, Lydia !

LYDIA. No !

MRS. BENNET. Kitty and Mary, you run and tell him ! And then both of you scurry along to the inn and fetch Wickham !

KITTY. Oh, here's a lark ! Come on, Mary !

(MARY *follows* KITTY *in a scrambling rush off.*)

MRS. BENNET. Now, my love, sit close to me and tell me the whole history ! When did the wedding happen ?

LYDIA. This very morning to be sure !

MRS. BENNET. Where from ?

LYDIA. Oh, Uncle and Aunt would have me to sleep last night in Gracechurch Street, so it could be said I was married from their house.

Mrs. Bennet. How kind and good they are !

Lydia. They were horried unpleasant all the time. Preaching away—however, I didn't hear above one word in ten. Such a fuss I was in for fear Wickham'd be late for a nine-o'clock wedding ! But when we reached the church porch, there he stood —the picture of an angel—in his blue coat, and Mr. Darcy in a brown one.

Jane. Mr. Darcy ?

Lydia. Oh, yes, Mr. Darcy, as stiff and tall and glum— Wickham was sure he'd treat us to a grand hotel breakfast— however, he was much too mean. Stalked off with a handshake for me and a bow for Wickham, the moment we left the church.

Mrs. Bennet. I'm amazed Mr. Darcy should attend such a quiet wedding, though it was of a Pemberley man.

Lydia. His father was Wickham's godfather, you know. And he was so bent on getting us tied up as quick as might be, he took no end of trouble with the special licence and everything.

Mrs. Bennet (delighted). A special licence ! Whatever next ? —But you haven't yet told us how you were run to earth ?

Lydia. Mr. Darcy knew where Wickham used to lodge. . . . At first, if you please, Mr. Darcy tried his hardest to get me away from Wickham !

Mrs. Bennet (horrified). Oh, scandalous !

Lydia. But I said, over and over, " Wickham is the one man in the world I love, and I shall never be happy without him, so I think it no harm to *hang on to* him."

Mrs. Bennet. Very right and proper.

Lydia. The horrid thing was, Wickham wouldn't have been so very unwilling to bid me good-bye.

Mrs. Bennet. I can't believe it !

Lydia. He always intended to marry an heiress, you know. I was half inclined to cry. But I up and reminded him, he wouldn't have much choice of heiresses in a debtors' prison, so he thought he might as well stick to me and see what Darcy was game for. So then Mr. Darcy fetched Uncle along, and the three of them battled it up and down, how much would Wickham take to make an honest woman of me. You'll laugh when I tell you how high Wickham made 'em go.—To start with, of course, he put the price out of all reason so as to bargain it down.

Elizabeth. How atrociously sordid !

Mrs. Bennet. What's the matter with you, Lizzy ? Why shouldn't Mr. Darcy advance money to his father's godson ?

Lydia. What Wickham hoped for was a fat living at Pemberley that's suddenly come into the market.—Wouldn't it have been a lark to see him dressed up in black and yaw-yaw-ing in the pulpit ?—However, Mr. Darcy wouldn't hear of it. In the end, Wickham agreed to a commission in the regulars. So my handsome husband will wear a red coat again, in spite of having to resign from the militia.

MRS. BENNET. And was it true about the poor fellow's debts ?

LYDIA. Oh, Mr. Darcy had to clear them off before he could buy the commission.

JANE. You frighten me, Lydia. What did the total sum amount to ?

LYDIA (*gaily triumphant*). Close on nine thousand pounds ! None of my sisters will have such a dowry.

ELIZABETH. Oh, how can papa ever repay ?

MRS. BENNET. " Papa repay ? " Stuff and nonsense !

ELIZABETH. Of course he will want to repay ! Lydia called it her dowry—" what he would take to make an honest woman " of her.

LYDIA. Papa is never to know ! That's the reason Mr. Darcy brought Uncle into it. They all mean papa to believe it was Uncle pulled Wickham out of the hole, and the cost but a few hundreds.

ELIZABETH. To hide the truth will not be easy.

JANE. You'll have to be careful, Lyddie.

LYDIA. Good Lord, I quite forgot ! Wickham forbade me to breathe a word about the money to anyone ! I promised them all I wouldn't so much as mention Mr. Darcy's name. For God's sake, don't let Wickham know I let it out ! He'd be so angry ! For he can't bear Mr. Darcy, and wouldn't have took a ha'p'ny from him if it weren't to revenge himself.

MRS. BENNET. T't, t't !

JANE. Oh, Lyddie, Lyddie ! What *has* Brighton done to you ?

LYDIA. How d'you mean ? Brighton's got me a prodigious handsome husband and a thumping dowry. I'm not surprised you envy me. I only hope you'll have half as good luck You ought to take them all to Brighton, mamma.

MRS. BENNET. If I have my way, I will, my dear. Is Wickham's new regiment to be quartered there ?

LYDIA. No. We are under orders to Newcastle.

MRS. BENNET. Oh, my love, that's a monstrous way off, is it not ?

LYDIA. Nearly to Scotland.

MRS. BENNET. My darling child ! Must you go so far ?

LYDIA. Oh, Lord, yes. There's nothing in that. We shall be at Newcastle all winter, and I dare say there will be some balls. Jane and Lizzy had better come and stay with me. I'll engage to get them husbands.

JANE. Thank you, but I would rather stay at home.

ELIZABETH. And I don't particularly care for your way of getting husbands.

LYDIA. La, you are so strange !

MRS. BENNET (*in sudden excitement*). Lyddie! You're forgetting your wedding-clothes!

LYDIA (*who has a certain fear of her father*). Will papa give me any money?

MRS. BENNET. Directly he comes in he shall write you a cheque!

LYDIA. Ho, ho! How fine I shall be!

MRS. BENNET. I've one length of pink muslin put by, upstairs.

LYDIA. Oh, come along and let me look!

MRS. BENNET (*letting herself be pulled to her feet*). Jane, you will have to find it for me.

JANE. I'm coming, ma'am.

LYDIA. You walk after me, Jane, now I'm a married woman.

JANE. I'm very glad to walk after you.

(*They are all three moving towards the door when MR. BINGLEY is announced.*)

MRS. BENNET. La, Mr. Bingley, how delighted I am! (*Giving him her hand, which he kisses.*) I'd an idea you'd turn up this morning.

BINGLEY. I trust I find you well?

MRS. BENNET. Remarkably well, I thank you. Jane hasn't been quite the thing since you went away, but she'll soon be herself again. . . . You haven't yet heard of the wedding in the family! My youngest, to Mr. Wickham. You remember a singularly noble-looking young officer?

BINGLEY (*who had bowed to all three girls, now shakes hands with LYDIA*). Pray accept my most cordial congratulations!

LYDIA (*giggling*). I'm vastly obliged.

MRS. BENNET. Take the armchair, Mr. Bingley, and put your hat and gloves out of your hand. . . . It is a delightful thing, to be sure, to have a daughter well married.

BINGLEY. Indeed it must be!

MRS. BENNET. But quite shocking to have her snatched away from me so soon. My son-in-law's new regiment is to be at Newcastle, which is quite northward it seems.

BINGLEY. Let us hope when your other daughters marry, Mrs. Bennet, they will not be so far removed.

MRS. BENNET. I pray Jane won't in any case. . . . You will be at Netherfield for the shooting, Mr. Bingley, I suppose?

BINGLEY. I suppose I shall.

MRS. BENNET. When you have killed all your own birds, I beg you will come here and shoot as many as you please on Mr. Bennet's manor.

BINGLEY. That is most kind of you, but I am not so rabid a sportsman.

ELIZABETH. How did you enjoy the season in town, Mr. Bingley?

BINGLEY. But so—so. It taught me that I vastly prefer country life. In March, I remember, Miss Bennet was planning to plant creepers on the hermitage. Was that done, I wonder ?

MRS. BENNET. Jane must show you.

BINGLEY. I should like it of all things !

JANE. Clematis and white jasmine were planted.

MRS. BENNET. Go now, my dear, your parasol is handy.

JANE. You will come too, Lizzy ?

ELIZABETH. I shall love to.

MRS. BENNET. Not you, Lizzy. I've something I want you to do upstairs. Most pressing and important.

(BINGLEY *is already handing* JANE *out through the conservatory.*)

ELIZABETH. Very well, ma'am. I can see the hermitage another time. . . . Dear madam, you do so embarrass Jane by these manœuvres. They only make her draw further into her shell.

MRS. BENNET. Nonsense ! It's you make the mischief by abetting her in her foolishness. If you had but played sisterly in the spring, Jane would have been mistress of Netherfield by now, and Lydia might have been married from there instead of from over a shop.

LYDIA. You fancy you can make men run after you by nothing but running away. Well, you can't. It's high time you two listened to mamma and me. We're not married women for nothing.

(*The* SERVANT *announces* LADY CATHERINE DE BOURGH, *and that august personage sweeps in. She is* " *a tall, large woman, with strongly marked features which may once have been handsome.*")

MRS. BENNET (*under her breath*). Gracious Heaven !

LYDIA (*less under her breath*). Good Lord !

ELIZABETH. Allow me to present my mamma, Mrs. Bennet— Lady Catherine de Bourgh.

MRS. BENNET. I am much honoured by your ladyship's visit.

LADY CATHERINE (*whose curtsies are haughtily distant*). I desire a private conversation with Miss Elizabeth Bennet.

MRS. BENNET. Oh, certainly, your ladyship. . . . Permit me to present my married daughter, Mrs. Wickham.—Possibly you are acquainted with Mr. Wickham, as he was godson to your late brother-in-law ?

LADY CATHERINE. I have heard of him as the son of the steward of my late brother-in-law.

MRS. BENNET (*with spirit*). I'd have you to know, madam, the present Mr. Darcy attended my daughter's wedding.

(*Her two daughters try, each after her fashion, to check further confidences.*)

LADY CATHERINE. Did he ?

MRS. BENNET. There's no harm in your ladyship's knowing.

LADY CATHERINE. It is right that I should. I am his aunt and entitled to know all his concerns.

MRS. BENNET. I believe Mr. Darcy has a great value for Mr. Wickham.

LADY CATHERINE. My belief does not chime with yours.

MRS. BENNET. As gentlemanly a young man as anybody ever met, and has a commission in the regulars, and the dowry he had with my Lydia was——

LYDIA. Oh, mamma.

MRS. BENNET. A very considerable sum.

LYDIA. You promised you'd come and see about my wedding-clothes !

LADY CATHERINE. Pray do not let me detain you, Mrs. Bennet, from the preparation of your married daughter's wedding-clothes.

MRS. BENNET (*confused*). Very kind of your ladyship, I am sure. . . . I trust the rest of your ladyship's journey will prove agreeable.

LYDIA (*pushing* MRS. BENNET *off*). On the way, ma'am, I'll show 'em my ring in the servant's hall.

(MRS. BENNET *and* LYDIA *depart.*)

LADY CATHERINE. Explain that reference to a dowry.

ELIZABETH. I am unable to.

LADY CATHERINE. Mr. Collins has mentioned to me more than once that you and your sisters were almost portionless. Who furnished the dowry ?

ELIZABETH. I should not feel justified in telling you, even if I knew.

LADY CATHERINE. Miss Bennet, I am not to be trifled with. However insincere you may choose to be, you will not find me so. My character has ever been celebrated for its frankness. . . . Yesterday I received a letter from my nephew, Mr. Darcy. In it he informed me that Wickham had been found and this marriage was arranged. How did my nephew know ? Has he been busying himself in the affair ?

ELIZABETH. May I ask why your questions should be addressed to me ?

LADY CATHERINE. These evasions will not help you, Miss Bennet. If my nephew did patch up your sister's disgraceful elopement, he did it to please you.

ELIZABETH. Your ladyship flatters me.

LADY CATHERINE. You are excessively impudent. . . . At the time of your stay at the rectory, I regarded you as a sensible young woman, and so much lower than my nephew that I kept no eye on your manner towards him, or his to you.

ELIZABETH. Again you flatter me.

LADY CATHERINE. Insolent girl! I would not injure my nephew so much as to believe it possible he could go the length of making you an offer of marriage.—But *has he*?

ELIZABETH. Your ladyship has declared it to be impossible.

LADY CATHERINE. It ought to be so; it must be so while he retains the use of his reason. But by your arts and allurements you may have drawn him in.

ELIZABETH. If I had, I should be the last person to confess it.

LADY CATHERINE. Let me be rightly understood. This match to which you have the presumption to aspire can never take place. No, never. Mr. Fitzwilliam Darcy is engaged to my daughter. Now what have you to say?

ELIZABETH. Only this: if he is so, why should you suppose he may have made an offer to me?

LADY CATHERINE (*after a pause*). The engagement is of a peculiar kind. From their cradles I destined them for one another.

ELIZABETH. An engagement so peculiar can hardly be binding. Is Mr. Darcy aware of its existence?

LADY CATHERINE. This is not to be endured! . . . Do you pay no regard to my wishes? Are you lost to every feeling of propriety and delicacy? . . . Tell me once for all, *are you engaged to him*?

ELIZABETH (*after a pause*). I am not.

LADY CATHERINE. Good! And you promise me never to enter into such an engagement?

ELIZABETH. I will make no promise whatever.

LADY CATHERINE. Miss Bennet, I am shocked and astonished. But do not deceive yourself into a belief that I will ever recede. I shall not go away until you have given me the assurance I require.

ELIZABETH. And I certainly never shall give it. I am not to be intimidated into anything so unreasonable. How far your nephew might approve of your interference in his affairs I cannot tell; but you have certainly no right to order mine.

LADY CATHERINE. Not so hasty, if you please. To the objections I have already urged——

(*The* SERVANT *announces* MR. FITZWILLIAM DARCY. *He is restraining rage.*)

DARCY (*after formal and brief salutations*). I saw your chaise at the door, Aunt Catherine, and learnt that you were calling on Miss Elizabeth Bennet.

LADY CATHERINE. And must I ask your leave before I call on Miss Elizabeth Bennet? . . . The truth is you were about to call on her yourself.

DARCY. With *her* leave—not yours—I am.

ELIZABETH. I beg you will be seated, sir, and lay your hat aside.

(*He accepts these invitations.*)

LADY CATHERINE. Fitzwilliam, I have this moment been hearing from Mrs. Bennet that you were at the wedding of her youngest daughter. And that someone supplied her with a dowry. *Was it you?*

DARCY. By what right, madam, do you make these inquiries into my actions ?

LADY CATHERINE (*stonily*). When a young gentleman of high standing promotes the marriage of an inferior and provides an endowment for the bride—the world is likely to suspect that his motives are not purely disinterested.

DARCY. Aunt Catherine, some garbled version of this affair seems to have reached both you and Miss Bennet. Let me explain. It is very simple. The news of Wickham's elopement overwhelmed me with remorse ; because I could have prevented it.

LADY CATHERINE. You ? How ?

DARCY. I had long known the man's character. A private word from me to Mr. Bennet and Colonel Forster would have made it impossible for him to become intimate in their families. Neglect of my duty led to a calamity. Naturally I had to do what lay in my power to set the wrong right.

LADY CATHERINE. So you paid Wickham's debts and bought him a commission and saw to it that the wedding was in order ? (DARCY *bows*.) Most quixotic and extravagant. But prompted by no sentiment beyond the wish to clear your conscience.—Take notice, Miss Bennet.

DARCY. I did not say that.

LADY CATHERINE. When you came in, Fitzwilliam, I was on the brink of an appeal to Miss Bennet to have some regard for your honour and credit.

DARCY. What on earth can you mean ?

LADY CATHERINE. Let me speak ! I was about to inform her that if you marry beneath you, your wife will be censured, slighted and despised by everyone connected with you.

DARCY. If I marry at all I shall not marry beneath me. My relations may be at ease on that score.

LADY CATHERINE. Don't lose your temper, Fitzwilliam ! Be calm. This girl has infatuated you, but I will save you yet !

DARCY. You are many weeks too late.

LADY CATHERINE. She told me she is not engaged to you.

DARCY. Miss Bennet rejected my offer.

LADY CATHERINE. Heaven and earth ! . . . Then why couldn't you promise me not to marry him ?

ELIZABETH. Because I did not consider you had the right to exact such a promise—even if I were willing to make it.

LADY CATHERINE. You are then resolved to have him ?

ELIZABETH. Are you presenting a proposal on Mr. Darcy's behalf ?

DARCY. Aunt Catherine ! I cannot allow you to proceed. I wish you to know that when Miss Bennet refused me, she gave me a most salutary lesson. On pride. On valuing myself for my birth, education, and fortune. I was properly humbled. Recently, while I was staying with you, I set myself to obtain her forgiveness and lessen her ill-opinion. Some day, perhaps, I may venture to hope——

(*He falters and glances at* ELIZABETH, *who lifts her head.*)

LADY CATHERINE. You smiled at him !—I saw you smile . . . Oh, my nephew, I conjure you by the noble name you bear ! Can Fitzwilliam Darcy, grandson of Lord Fitzwilliam, contemplate matrimony with one whose sister has been the mistress of the son of his father's steward ?

DARCY. I must take the liberty, Miss Bennet, of ringing the bell, that my aunt may be shown to her carriage. (*He does so.*)

LADY CATHERINE. Attend me yourself, sir.

DARCY. I will not.

(*He opens the door for her.*)

LADY CATHERINE (*sailing off without a glance at* ELIZABETH). Marry her then ! Ruin yourself ! *I* have done with you !

(*He shuts the door upon her, and stands irresolute for a moment.*)

DARCY. Will you marry me ?

ELIZABETH. We have your aunt's express permission. (*By a gesture she checks his advance towards her.*) But can you forgive me all my wicked abuse of you—my pertness and sauciness and stupid, stupid prejudice ?

DARCY. I have nothing to forgive—everything to be forgiven.

(*She holds out both her hands ; he takes and kisses them.*)

(*The situation is unnoticed by* JANE, *who comes in from the hall, absorbed in her own happiness.*)

JANE. I want you to be first, Lizzy, to know that—— Oh, Mr. Darcy ? (*She curtsies to him parenthetically.*) Charles has gone to papa to ask his consent !

ELIZABETH (*embracing her*). Oh, Jane, darling !

DARCY. May I say how very glad I am ?

(*He shakes hands with* JANE. BINGLEY *runs in from the hall.*)

BINGLEY. Where is she ? . . . Jane, your father has no objection !

JANE. I was confident he would be pleased.

ELIZABETH (*shaking hands with him*). I am delighted that you are to be my brother.

DARCY (*shaking hands with him*). Splendid ! Splendid ! . . . *I* want to see Mr. Bennet——

(*He hurries off.*)

JANE. Why, Lizzy, I didn't notice it was odd Mr. Darcy was here—what brought him ?—Oh, can it be true ?

ELIZABETH. Quite, quite true ! Incredibly true !

(*Again the two embrace.*)

BINGLEY (*shaking hands with* ELIZABETH). This completes our happiness.

JANE. I must hasten to tell my dear mother. Will you come with me, Lizzy ?

ELIZABETH. The news must be broken gently. Tell her yours first. . . . Tell her mine too, if you will.

JANE. I shall love to.

(*She goes into the hall.*)

ELIZABETH (*dropping into a chair*). These floods of joy are almost overwhelming.

BINGLEY. I had no conception of the meaning of rapture until now ! Yet it is torture to recollect that I caused Jane to suffer. Darcy misled me—unwittingly. He fancied she was in peril of marrying me from sheer sweetness of temper. He was convinced by her perfect self-possession that she did not love me. But he has confessed that he might have been mistaken. She has told me he was.

ELIZABETH. What a friend he is ! What a pair of friends you and he are !

BINGLEY. Why do you laugh ?

ELIZABETH. I love to laugh at those I love.

(MR. BENNET *comes in from the hall, looking thoroughly worried.*)

MR. BENNET. Elizabeth !—Bingley, I must have a word with my daughter.

BINGLEY. Certainly, sir.

(*The door into the conservatory has been standing open since* JANE *came in.* BINGLEY *is gone in a moment, shutting the door after him.*)

MR. BENNET. Lizzy, are you out of your senses to be accepting this man ? Have you not always hated him ?

ELIZABETH. At first I'm afraid I did. I misjudged him shockingly. Now that I have come to know what he really is— I'm afraid I'm at the opposite extreme of feeling.

Mr. Bennet (*refusing to be won by her smile*). In other words, you are determined to have him. He is rich, to be sure. You may have three times as many fine clothes and fine carriages as Jane. But will they make you happy ?

Elizabeth. Oh, sir ? Those considerations do not weigh with me ! Have you any other objection than your belief of my indifference ?

Mr. Bennet. None whatever. Apart from his excellent taste in book-collecting, I know him only as a proud, unpleasant sort of man. But this would be nothing if you really liked him.

Elizabeth. I do, I do like him. (*Tearfully.*) Indeed he has no improper pride. He is perfectly amiable. Do not pain me by speaking of him in such terms.

Mr. Bennet. Lizzy, I have given him my consent. He is the kind of man, indeed, to whom I should never dare refuse anything he condescended to ask. I now give it to *you*, if you are resolved on having him. But let me advise you to think better of it. I know your disposition, Lizzy. Your lively talents would place you in the greatest danger in an unequal marriage. You could scarcely escape misery. My child, let me not have the grief of seeing *you* unable to respect your partner in life. You know not what you are about.

Elizabeth. Dear papa !—It is you who are ignorant of his worth. There are instances of his nobility of character which I may not tell you about without his leave. Some day you shall know.

Mr. Bennet (*judicially*). Do you truly esteem him, Lizzy ? Do you look up to him as your superior ?

Elizabeth. I do ! I do !

Mr. Bennet (*after a moment, permitting himself to be whimsical*). In everything but wit ?

Elizabeth (*soberly*). I do not think him witty.

Mr. Bennet. Ah, then you have preserved some balance. And you do honestly like him ?

Elizabeth. I love him.

Mr. Bennet. Then I can only trust he will prove worthy of you.

Elizabeth. If only I can be worthy of him !

Mr. Bennet. Bless my soul !

(*He kisses her affectionately.*)

Elizabeth (*clinging to him*). My dear, dear father !

Mr. Bennet. Spare me more of these gratifying shocks ! Within one short half-hour, Lydia is discovered to be married, Jane happy, and Elizabeth humble.

(*Father and daughter laugh together. Mrs. Bennet whirls in.*)

Mrs. Bennet. Oh, Mr. Bennet, did anyone ever hear the

like ? (*Crescendo.*) Lydia, Wickham !—but that's a trifle— Jane, *Netherfield* ! !   Lizzy, PEMBERLEY ! ! !   Oh, my sweetest Lizzy ! (*Folding her in an embrace.*)   Never did I dream that you would outdo Jane !   And the surprise !   Mr. Darcy, by all that's wonderful !   Lord bless me !   Ten thousand a year and very likely more !   Such a charming man !   So tall !   A house in town !   Jane's fortune is nothing to it, nothing at all !

(JANE *has slipped in unobtrusively, for* MRS. BENNET *left the door open.*)

ELIZABETH (*struggling free*).   Thank you, ma'am, thank you.

MR. BENNET.   Yet Jane will never believe she has cause for envy, will you, my dear ?

JANE.   Envy, sir ?—No ! . . .   I thank you for your goodness.

(*Having returned his kiss,* JANE *makes for the conservatory.*)

MRS. BENNET (*murmuring through the above*).   Marvel of marvels !   Oh, I shall go distracted ! . . .   Where are you off to, Jane ?

JANE (*by the conservatory door*).   He is out by the copse, ma'am.

MRS. BENNET.   Very right and proper. . . .   Where are you off to, Lizzy ?

ELIZABETH (*by the passage-door*).   He is in the library, ma'am.

MR. BENNET.   Take him out of it !   Into the hermitage if Jane is in the copse.

(*The two girls curtsy, wave to one another and go out,* R. *and* L.)

MRS. BENNET.   Three daughters married !   Oh, Mr. Bennet, how can you be so cool ?

MR. BENNET.   I have yet to greet Lydia.   Where is she ?

MRS. BENNET.   Dashed off to meet Wickham, on his way up from the inn with Mary and Kitty who I sent to fetch him.

MR. BENNET.   Then I need not be disturbed again before dinner.   Would it suit your nerves, my dear, to give me a kiss ?

MRS. BENNET (*affectionately—not passionately—complying with the suggestion*).   Oh, Mr. Bennet, how good you are !

MR. BENNET (*going, pauses*).   By the by, if any young men come for Mary or Kitty, send them in to me.   I am quite at leisure.

(*He goes out.*)

MRS. BENNET (*standing* C.).   One, two, three daughters married ! (*Expressive movements of her hands have ended with them lightly crossed on her breast.   Her aspiration is a wish rather than a prayer, but her gaze is directed a little upwards.*)   Four, five daughters married !

CURTAIN.